SEARCH & LEARN™

AROUND THE WORLD

BY TONY TALLARICO

Visit us at www.kidsbooks.com

CONTENTS

INTRODUCTION

How would you like to take a trip around the world? You don't need a ship, plane, or train ticket to visit all seven continents and every one of the world's 193 independent countries. All you have to do is explore this book!

Each colorful illustration zooms in on a particular area of the globe. Jump-start your journey by reading each map's introduction. Then check out the list of fun items hidden in the map. While you search for those items, you'll learn all sorts of cool facts about every country and region on Earth. No wonder the book is called *Search & Learn: Around the World*!

Two special maps will help you along your way. The world map on the opposite page gives you all seven continents at a glance. The United States map on p. 54 does the same for all 50 states.

Why wait any longer to start that around-the-world trip? Ready, set, turn the page!

ASIA, AUSTRALIA, AND OCEANIA

Asia, the largest of the continents, stretches from above the Arctic Circle to below the equator, and from the Ural Mountains in the east to the Pacific Ocean in the west. Asia's lands include some of the coldest, hottest, wettest, and driest places on Earth.

South and east of Asia lie Australia, New Zealand, and many small island nations in the Pacific, most south of the equator. Together, they form a region that is known as Oceania.

LEARN ABOUT ASIA, AUSTRALIA, AND OCEANIA AS YOU LOOK FOR THESE FUN ITEMS:

- ❑ Bird
- ❑ Coffeepot
- ❑ Elephant
- ❑ Gold
- ❑ Kangaroo
- ❑ Lobster
- ❑ Mermaid
- ❑ Mountain climber
- ❑ Octopus
- ❑ Oil well
- ❑ Penguin
- ❑ Polar bear
- ❑ Sailboat
- ❑ Telescope

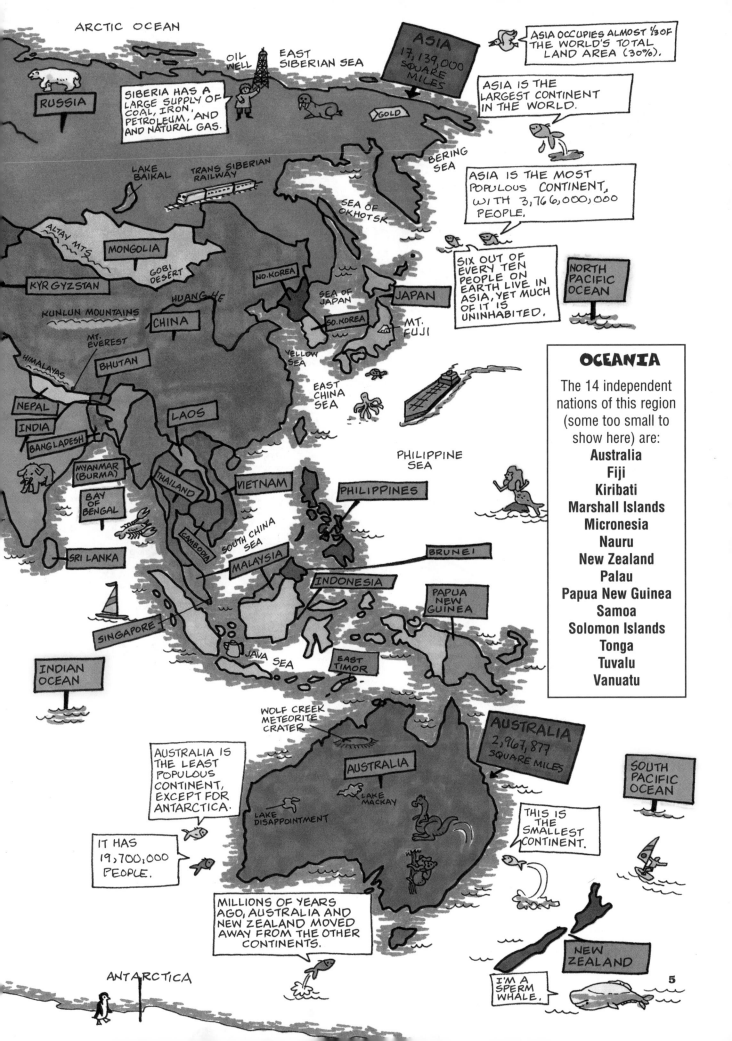

RUSSIA TAKES UP ONE SEVENTH OF THE WORLD'S TOTAL LAND AREA AND HAS THE SIXTH LARGEST POPULATION.

TWO THIRDS OF RUSSIA'S POPULATION LIVES IN EUROPE, WHILE ONLY A THIRD LIVES IN ASIA.

SNOW COVERS MORE THAN HALF OF RUSSIA FOR SIX MONTHS OF THE YEAR.

KARA SEA

BARENTS SEA

RUSSIA

FORESTS COVER MORE THAN HALF THE COUNTRY.

WHITE SEA

CARS AND TRACTORS MANUFACTURING

URAL MTS.

THE URAL MTS. DIVIDE RUSSIA BETWEEN EUROPE AND ASIA.

YENISEY RIVER

LAKE ONEGA

BALTIC SEA

LAKE LADOGA

ST. BASIL'S CATHEDRAL

GULF OF FINLAND

POTATOES

WHEAT

MOSCOW

BOLSHOI BALLET

THE REGION THAT LIES BETWEEN THE BLACK SEA AND THE CASPIAN SEA IS CALLED THE CAUCASUS.

OUR COUNTRY IS MAINLY STEPPE (A VAST SEMI-ARID PLAIN), DESERT, AND MOUNTAIN.

OUR POPULATION IS 14,800,000.

OUR LANGUAGES ARE KAZAKH AND RUSSIAN.

WE ARE ALMOST TWICE THE SIZE OF ALASKA.

GEORGIA'S POPULATION IS 4,400,000.

ITS WARM CLIMATE ATTRACTS TOURISTS.

ITS LANGUAGES ARE GEORGIAN, RUSSIAN, ARMENIAN, AND AZERI.

KAZAKHSTAN

THE MAIN SPACE CENTER FOR THE COMMONWEALTH IS LOCATED HERE.

ALTAY MTS.

TBILISI

OIL

CASPIAN SEA

UZBEKISTAN

ASTANA

95% OF OUR COUNTRY IS MOUNTAINOUS.

BLACK SEA

TASHKENT

BISHKEK

KYRGYZSTAN

GEORGIA

BAKU

ASHGABAT

90% IS COVERED BY KARA-KUM DESERT.

COMMUNISM PEAK (24,590 FT)

ARMENIA

YEREVAN

AZERBAIJAN

TURKMENISTAN

TAJIKISTAN

OUR POPULATION IS 6,300,000, AND OUR LANGUAGE IS TAJIK (ALSO RUSSIAN).

MEDITERRANEAN SEA

DUSHANBE

THE LANGUAGES OF AZERBAIJAN ARE AZERI, RUSSIAN, AND ARMENIAN.

THEIR POPULATION IS 8,200,000.

ARMENIA IS THE MOST INDUSTRIALIZED STATE IN THE CAUCASUS.

TURKMENISTAN'S POPULATION IS 5,600,000, AND ITS LANGUAGES ARE TURKMEN, RUSSIAN, AND UZBEK.

ITS POPULATION IS 3,800,000.

MAIN LANGUAGES SPOKEN ARE ARMENIAN AND RUSSIAN.

RUSSIA AND ITS NEIGHBORS

Russia, the world's largest country, spans two continents. It covers more than 50 percent of Europe and more than 35 percent of Asia.

Russia used to be part of an even bigger nation called the Soviet Union, which broke apart in 1991. Many of the countries to Russia's south, now independent, also were part of the Soviet Union until 1991.

EUROPE

ASIA

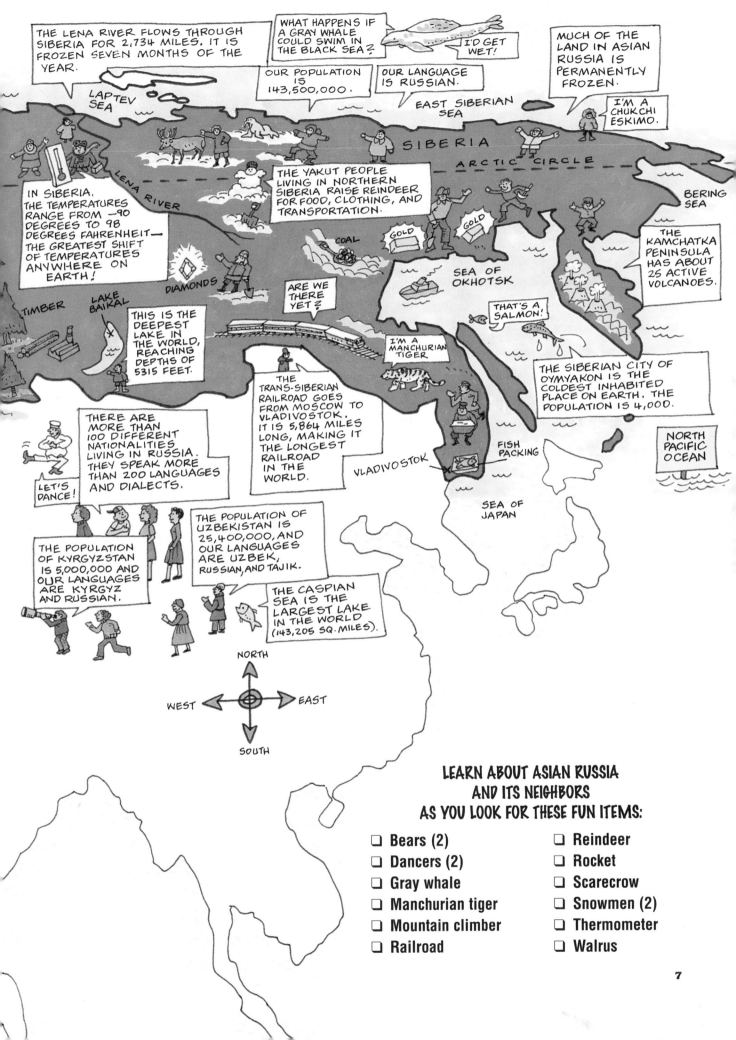

THE LENA RIVER FLOWS THROUGH SIBERIA FOR 2,734 MILES. IT IS FROZEN SEVEN MONTHS OF THE YEAR.

WHAT HAPPENS IF A GRAY WHALE COULD SWIM IN THE BLACK SEA?

I'D GET WET!

OUR POPULATION IS 143,500,000.

OUR LANGUAGE IS RUSSIAN.

MUCH OF THE LAND IN ASIAN RUSSIA IS PERMANENTLY FROZEN.

I'M A CHUKCHI ESKIMO.

LAPTEV SEA

EAST SIBERIAN SEA

SIBERIA

ARCTIC CIRCLE

BERING SEA

LENA RIVER

IN SIBERIA, THE TEMPERATURES RANGE FROM −90 DEGREES TO 98 DEGREES FAHRENHEIT—THE GREATEST SHIFT OF TEMPERATURES ANYWHERE ON EARTH!

THE YAKUT PEOPLE LIVING IN NORTHERN SIBERIA RAISE REINDEER FOR FOOD, CLOTHING, AND TRANSPORTATION.

COAL

GOLD

GOLD

THE KAMCHATKA PENINSULA HAS ABOUT 25 ACTIVE VOLCANOES.

DIAMONDS

SEA OF OKHOTSK

TIMBER

LAKE BAIKAL

THIS IS THE DEEPEST LAKE IN THE WORLD, REACHING DEPTHS OF 5315 FEET.

ARE WE THERE YET?

THAT'S A SALMON!

I'M A MANCHURIAN TIGER

THE SIBERIAN CITY OF OYMYAKON IS THE COLDEST INHABITED PLACE ON EARTH. THE POPULATION IS 4,000.

THE TRANS-SIBERIAN RAILROAD GOES FROM MOSCOW TO VLADIVOSTOK. IT IS 5,864 MILES LONG, MAKING IT THE LONGEST RAILROAD IN THE WORLD.

THERE ARE MORE THAN 100 DIFFERENT NATIONALITIES LIVING IN RUSSIA. THEY SPEAK MORE THAN 200 LANGUAGES AND DIALECTS.

LET'S DANCE!

FISH PACKING

VLADIVOSTOK

NORTH PACIFIC OCEAN

THE POPULATION OF UZBEKISTAN IS 25,400,000, AND OUR LANGUAGES ARE UZBEK, RUSSIAN, AND TAJIK.

SEA OF JAPAN

THE POPULATION OF KYRGYZSTAN IS 5,000,000 AND OUR LANGUAGES ARE KYRGYZ AND RUSSIAN.

THE CASPIAN SEA IS THE LARGEST LAKE IN THE WORLD (143,205 SQ. MILES).

NORTH

WEST

EAST

SOUTH

LEARN ABOUT ASIAN RUSSIA AND ITS NEIGHBORS AS YOU LOOK FOR THESE FUN ITEMS:

- ❏ Bears (2)
- ❏ Dancers (2)
- ❏ Gray whale
- ❏ Manchurian tiger
- ❏ Mountain climber
- ❏ Railroad
- ❏ Reindeer
- ❏ Rocket
- ❏ Scarecrow
- ❏ Snowmen (2)
- ❏ Thermometer
- ❏ Walrus

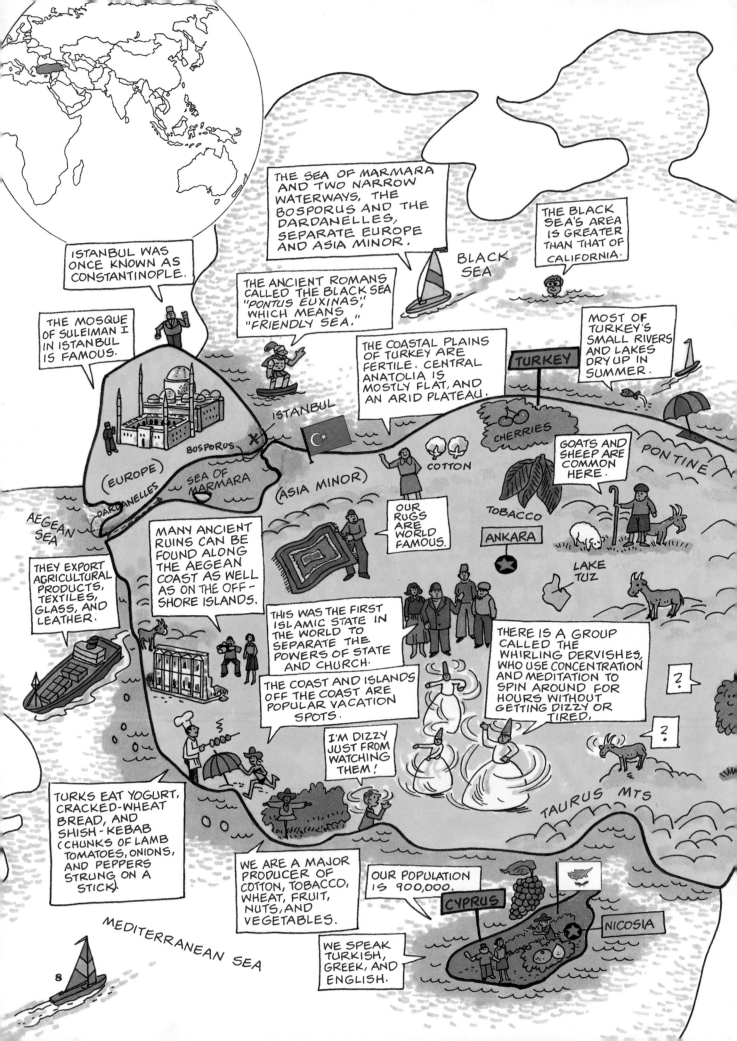

TURKEY AND CYPRUS

Three percent of Turkey's land area lies in Europe. The rest is in Asia, in a region known as Anatolia or Asia Minor. Istanbul, which is Turkey's largest city, is the only city in the world that occupies land on two continents.

Cyprus is only 140 miles long at its longest point, and 60 miles wide at its widest point. It has long been controlled by other nations, and Greece and Turkey both still claim parts of it.

LEARN ABOUT TURKEY AND CYPRUS AS YOU LOOK FOR THESE FUN ITEMS:

- ❏ Apples
- ❏ Ball
- ❏ Bears (3)
- ❏ Book
- ❏ Cook
- ❏ Cowboy
- ❏ Egg
- ❏ Fish
- ❏ Goats (5)
- ❏ Grapes
- ❏ Ibis
- ❏ Ladder
- ❏ Sailboats (3)
- ❏ Shepherd
- ❏ Tea bag
- ❏ Telescope
- ❏ Tin Man
- ❏ Umbrellas (2)

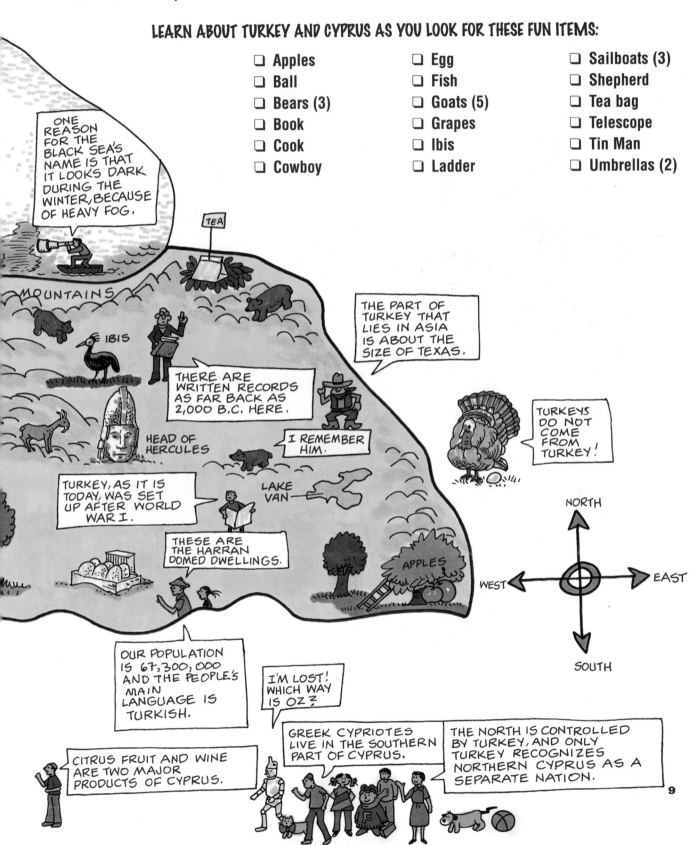

ONE REASON FOR THE BLACK SEA'S NAME IS THAT IT LOOKS DARK DURING THE WINTER, BECAUSE OF HEAVY FOG.

TEA

MOUNTAINS

IBIS

THE PART OF TURKEY THAT LIES IN ASIA IS ABOUT THE SIZE OF TEXAS.

THERE ARE WRITTEN RECORDS AS FAR BACK AS 2,000 B.C. HERE.

HEAD OF HERCULES

I REMEMBER HIM.

TURKEYS DO NOT COME FROM TURKEY!

TURKEY, AS IT IS TODAY, WAS SET UP AFTER WORLD WAR I.

LAKE VAN

THESE ARE THE HARRAN DOMED DWELLINGS.

APPLES

NORTH
WEST — EAST
SOUTH

OUR POPULATION IS 67,300,000 AND THE PEOPLE'S MAIN LANGUAGE IS TURKISH.

I'M LOST! WHICH WAY IS OZ?

CITRUS FRUIT AND WINE ARE TWO MAJOR PRODUCTS OF CYPRUS.

GREEK CYPRIOTES LIVE IN THE SOUTHERN PART OF CYPRUS.

THE NORTH IS CONTROLLED BY TURKEY, AND ONLY TURKEY RECOGNIZES NORTHERN CYPRUS AS A SEPARATE NATION.

THE MIDDLE EAST

This part of Asia, in the area between the Tigris and Euphrates rivers, was one of the first places where civilization was recorded. Towns and communities were thriving here 6,000 years ago. The Arabian Peninsula *(see pp. 12-13)* is also part of the Middle East—a region that has about 75 percent of the world's oil reserves.

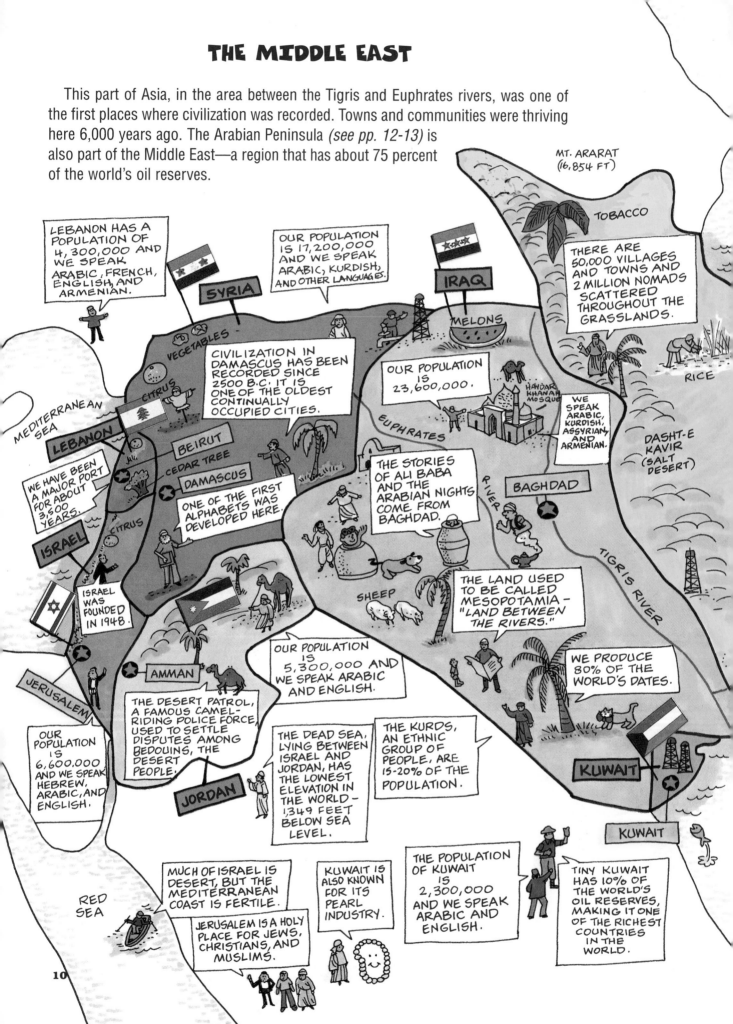

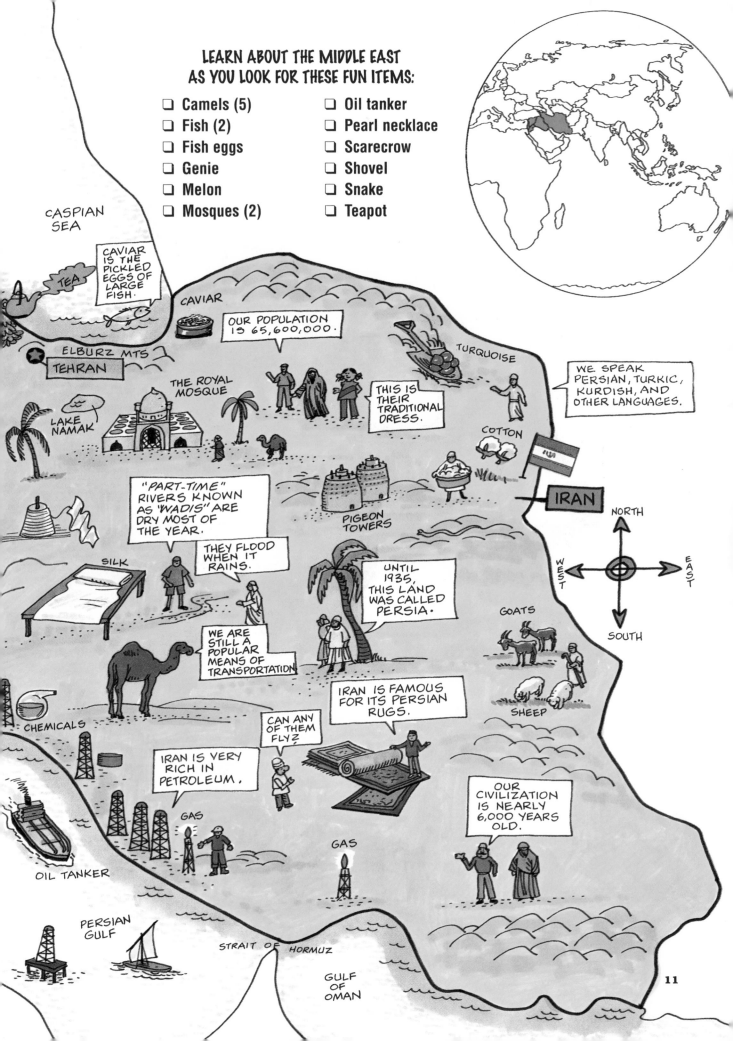

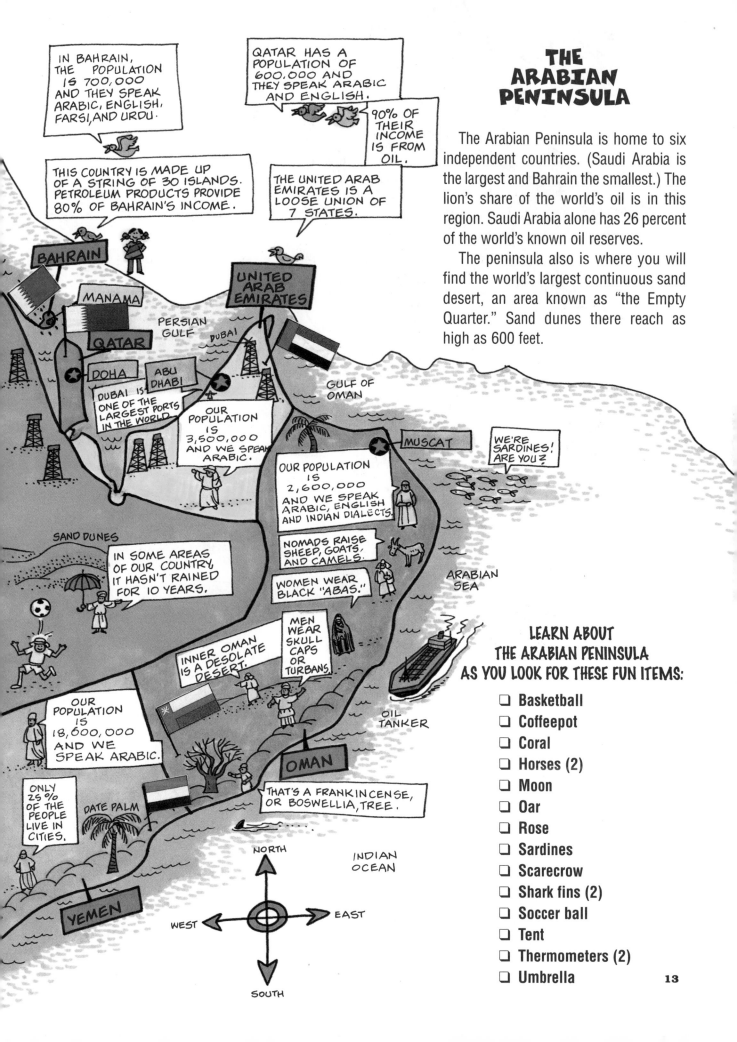

THE ARABIAN PENINSULA

The Arabian Peninsula is home to six independent countries. (Saudi Arabia is the largest and Bahrain the smallest.) The lion's share of the world's oil is in this region. Saudi Arabia alone has 26 percent of the world's known oil reserves.

The peninsula also is where you will find the world's largest continuous sand desert, an area known as "the Empty Quarter." Sand dunes there reach as high as 600 feet.

LEARN ABOUT
THE ARABIAN PENINSULA
AS YOU LOOK FOR THESE FUN ITEMS:

- ☐ Basketball
- ☐ Coffeepot
- ☐ Coral
- ☐ Horses (2)
- ☐ Moon
- ☐ Oar
- ☐ Rose
- ☐ Sardines
- ☐ Scarecrow
- ☐ Shark fins (2)
- ☐ Soccer ball
- ☐ Tent
- ☐ Thermometers (2)
- ☐ Umbrella

13

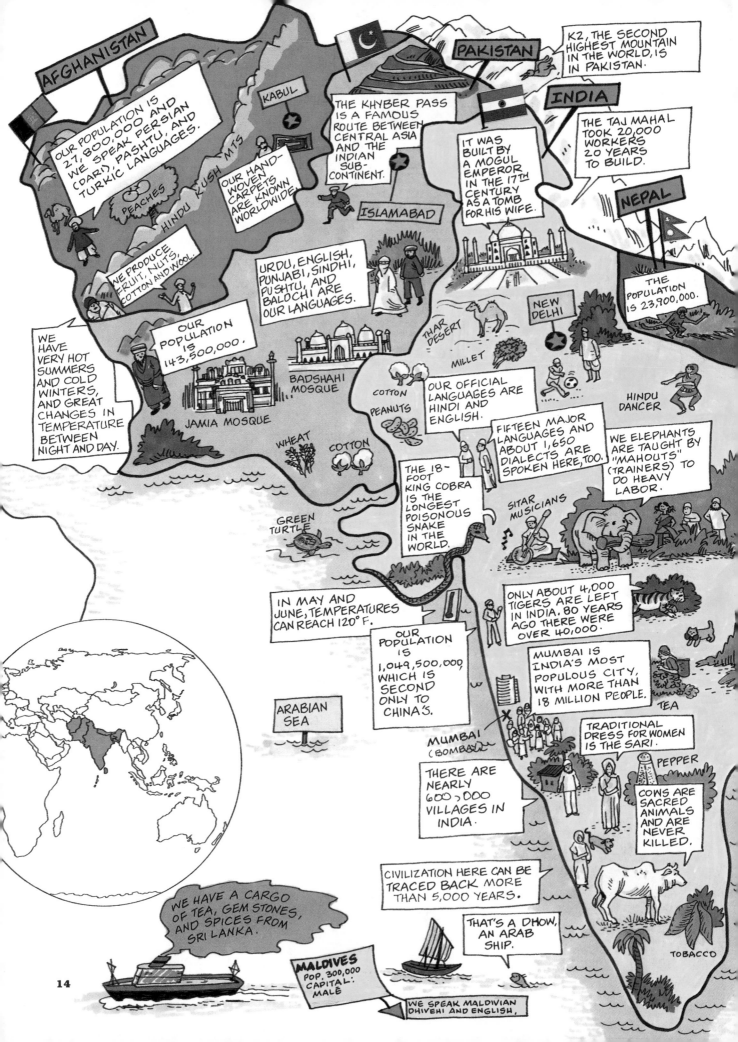

AFGHANISTAN

OUR POPULATION IS 27,800,000 AND WE SPEAK PERSIAN (DARI), PASHTU, AND TURKIC LANGUAGES.

KABUL

OUR HAND-WOVEN CARPETS ARE KNOWN WORLDWIDE.

HINDU KUSH MTS

PEACHES

WE PRODUCE FRUIT, NUTS, COTTON AND WOOL.

PAKISTAN

THE KHYBER PASS IS A FAMOUS ROUTE BETWEEN CENTRAL ASIA AND THE INDIAN SUB-CONTINENT.

ISLAMABAD

K2, THE SECOND HIGHEST MOUNTAIN IN THE WORLD, IS IN PAKISTAN.

INDIA

IT WAS BUILT BY A MOGUL EMPEROR IN THE 17TH CENTURY AS A TOMB FOR HIS WIFE.

THE TAJ MAHAL TOOK 20,000 WORKERS 20 YEARS TO BUILD.

NEPAL

THE POPULATION IS 23,900,000.

URDU, ENGLISH, PUNJABI, SINDHI, PUSHTU, AND BALOCHI ARE OUR LANGUAGES.

WE HAVE VERY HOT SUMMERS AND COLD WINTERS, AND GREAT CHANGES IN TEMPERATURE BETWEEN NIGHT AND DAY.

OUR POPULATION IS 143,500,000.

BADSHAHI MOSQUE

COTTON

PEANUTS

THAR DESERT

NEW DELHI

MILLET

OUR OFFICIAL LANGUAGES ARE HINDI AND ENGLISH.

HINDU DANCER

WE ELEPHANTS ARE TAUGHT BY "MAHOUTS" (TRAINERS) TO DO HEAVY LABOR.

JAMIA MOSQUE

WHEAT

COTTON

THE 18-FOOT KING COBRA IS THE LONGEST POISONOUS SNAKE IN THE WORLD.

FIFTEEN MAJOR LANGUAGES AND ABOUT 1,650 DIALECTS ARE SPOKEN HERE, TOO.

GREEN TURTLE

SITAR MUSICIANS

IN MAY AND JUNE, TEMPERATURES CAN REACH 120° F.

ONLY ABOUT 4,000 TIGERS ARE LEFT IN INDIA. 80 YEARS AGO THERE WERE OVER 40,000.

OUR POPULATION IS 1,049,500,000, WHICH IS SECOND ONLY TO CHINA'S.

MUMBAI IS INDIA'S MOST POPULOUS CITY, WITH MORE THAN 18 MILLION PEOPLE.

ARABIAN SEA

MUMBAI (BOMBAY)

TEA

TRADITIONAL DRESS FOR WOMEN IS THE SARI.

THERE ARE NEARLY 600,000 VILLAGES IN INDIA.

PEPPER

COWS ARE SACRED ANIMALS AND ARE NEVER KILLED.

CIVILIZATION HERE CAN BE TRACED BACK MORE THAN 5,000 YEARS.

WE HAVE A CARGO OF TEA, GEM STONES, AND SPICES FROM SRI LANKA.

THAT'S A DHOW, AN ARAB SHIP.

MALDIVES
POP. 300,000
CAPITAL: MALÉ

TOBACCO

WE SPEAK MALDIVIAN DHIVEHI AND ENGLISH.

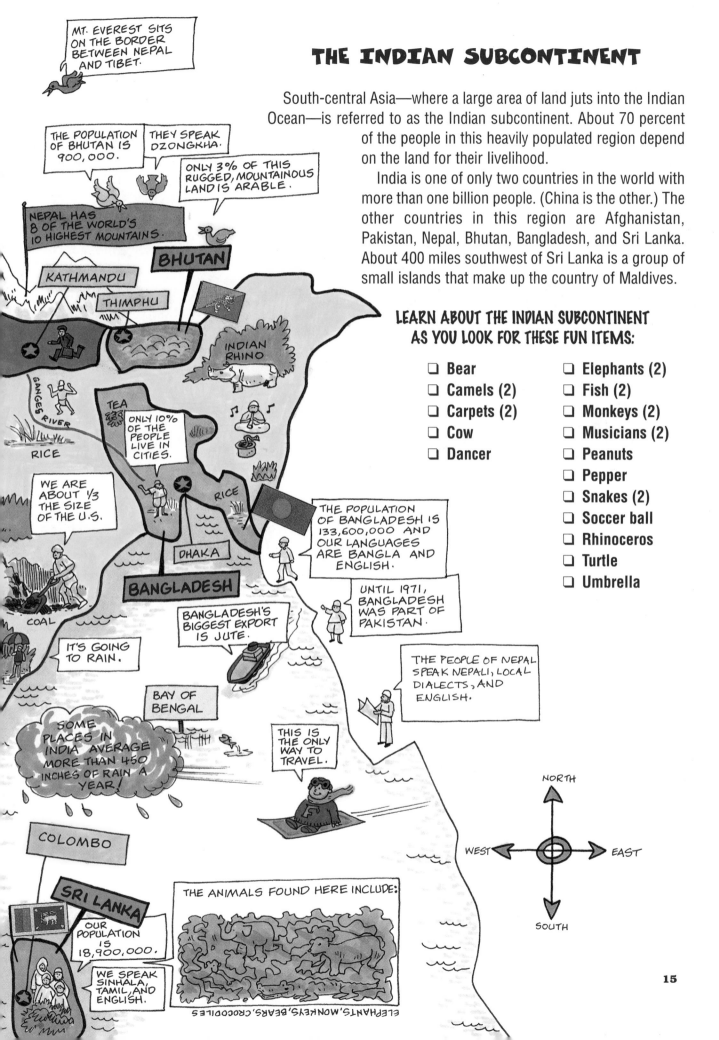

THE INDIAN SUBCONTINENT

South-central Asia—where a large area of land juts into the Indian Ocean—is referred to as the Indian subcontinent. About 70 percent of the people in this heavily populated region depend on the land for their livelihood.

India is one of only two countries in the world with more than one billion people. (China is the other.) The other countries in this region are Afghanistan, Pakistan, Nepal, Bhutan, Bangladesh, and Sri Lanka. About 400 miles southwest of Sri Lanka is a group of small islands that make up the country of Maldives.

LEARN ABOUT THE INDIAN SUBCONTINENT AS YOU LOOK FOR THESE FUN ITEMS:

- ❏ Bear
- ❏ Camels (2)
- ❏ Carpets (2)
- ❏ Cow
- ❏ Dancer
- ❏ Elephants (2)
- ❏ Fish (2)
- ❏ Monkeys (2)
- ❏ Musicians (2)
- ❏ Peanuts
- ❏ Pepper
- ❏ Snakes (2)
- ❏ Soccer ball
- ❏ Rhinoceros
- ❏ Turtle
- ❏ Umbrella

MT. EVEREST SITS ON THE BORDER BETWEEN NEPAL AND TIBET.

THE POPULATION OF BHUTAN IS 900,000.

THEY SPEAK DZONGKHA.

ONLY 3% OF THIS RUGGED, MOUNTAINOUS LAND IS ARABLE.

NEPAL HAS 8 OF THE WORLD'S 10 HIGHEST MOUNTAINS.

BHUTAN

KATHMANDU

THIMPHU

INDIAN RHINO

GANGES RIVER

RICE

TEA

ONLY 10% OF THE PEOPLE LIVE IN CITIES.

WE ARE ABOUT 1/3 THE SIZE OF THE U.S.

RICE

DHAKA

THE POPULATION OF BANGLADESH IS 133,600,000 AND OUR LANGUAGES ARE BANGLA AND ENGLISH.

BANGLADESH

UNTIL 1971, BANGLADESH WAS PART OF PAKISTAN.

COAL

BANGLADESH'S BIGGEST EXPORT IS JUTE.

IT'S GOING TO RAIN.

THE PEOPLE OF NEPAL SPEAK NEPALI, LOCAL DIALECTS, AND ENGLISH.

BAY OF BENGAL

SOME PLACES IN INDIA AVERAGE MORE THAN 450 INCHES OF RAIN A YEAR!

THIS IS THE ONLY WAY TO TRAVEL.

NORTH

WEST

EAST

SOUTH

COLOMBO

SRI LANKA

OUR POPULATION IS 18,900,000.

WE SPEAK SINHALA, TAMIL, AND ENGLISH.

THE ANIMALS FOUND HERE INCLUDE:

ELEPHANTS, MONKEYS, BEARS, CROCODILES

15

CHINA and NORTHEASTERN ASIA

China is the world's third-largest country in land area and first in population. (One out of every five people on Earth lives in China.) Much of China and the Korean peninsula is mountainous. The world's highest mountains, the Himalayas, are in Tibet, a region of China.

LEARN ABOUT CHINA AND NORTHEASTERN ASIA AS YOU LOOK FOR THESE FUN ITEMS:

- ☐ Bicycles (5)
- ☐ Camel
- ☐ Clay soldiers
- ☐ Ducks (3)
- ☐ Flying saucer
- ☐ Genghis Khan
- ☐ Horse
- ☐ Junk
- ☐ Mongol tent
- ☐ Pandas (2)
- ☐ Vulture
- ☐ Yaks (2)

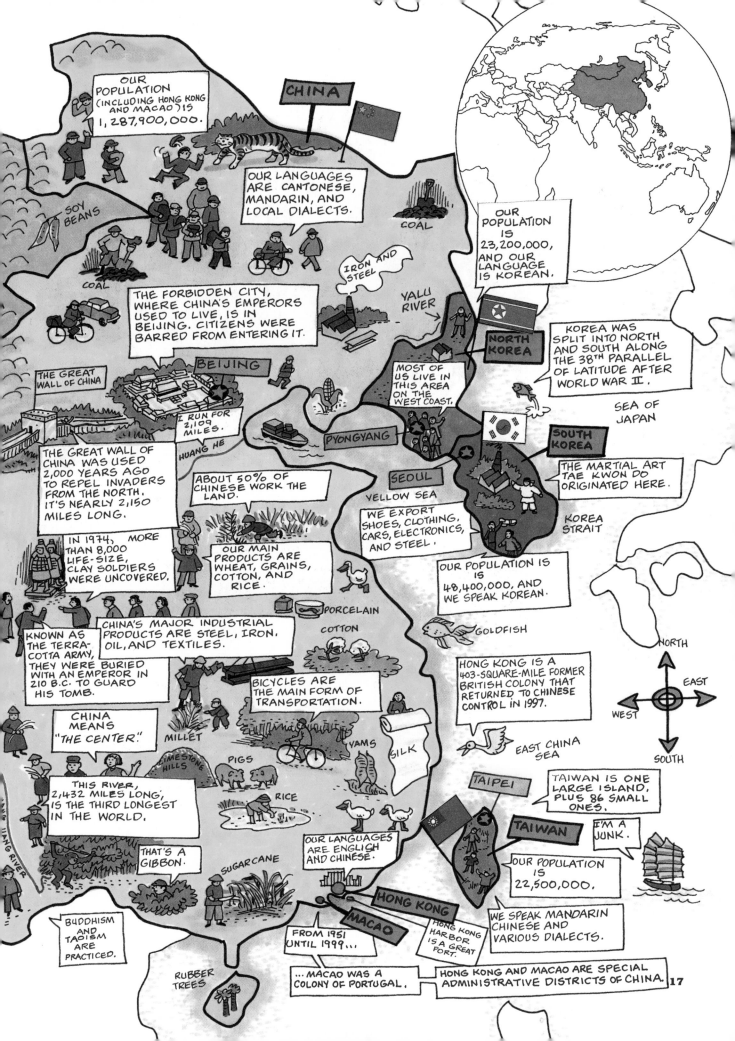

OUR POPULATION (INCLUDING HONG KONG AND MACAO) IS 1,287,900,000.

CHINA

OUR LANGUAGES ARE CANTONESE, MANDARIN, AND LOCAL DIALECTS.

SOY BEANS

COAL

COAL

OUR POPULATION IS 23,200,000, AND OUR LANGUAGE IS KOREAN.

IRON AND STEEL

YALU RIVER

THE FORBIDDEN CITY, WHERE CHINA'S EMPERORS USED TO LIVE, IS IN BEIJING. CITIZENS WERE BARRED FROM ENTERING IT.

NORTH KOREA

KOREA WAS SPLIT INTO NORTH AND SOUTH ALONG THE 38TH PARALLEL OF LATITUDE AFTER WORLD WAR II.

THE GREAT WALL OF CHINA

BEIJING

MOST OF US LIVE IN THIS AREA ON THE WEST COAST.

SEA OF JAPAN

I RUN FOR 2,109 MILES.

HUANG HE

PYONGYANG

SOUTH KOREA

THE GREAT WALL OF CHINA WAS USED 2,000 YEARS AGO TO REPEL INVADERS FROM THE NORTH. IT'S NEARLY 2,150 MILES LONG.

ABOUT 50% OF CHINESE WORK THE LAND.

SEOUL

THE MARTIAL ART TAE KWON DO ORIGINATED HERE.

YELLOW SEA

IN 1974, MORE THAN 8,000 LIFE-SIZE CLAY SOLDIERS WERE UNCOVERED.

OUR MAIN PRODUCTS ARE WHEAT, GRAINS, COTTON, AND RICE.

WE EXPORT SHOES, CLOTHING, CARS, ELECTRONICS, AND STEEL.

KOREA STRAIT

PORCELAIN

COTTON

OUR POPULATION IS 48,400,000, AND WE SPEAK KOREAN.

KNOWN AS THE TERRA-COTTA ARMY, THEY WERE BURIED WITH AN EMPEROR IN 210 B.C. TO GUARD HIS TOMB.

CHINA'S MAJOR INDUSTRIAL PRODUCTS ARE STEEL, IRON, OIL, AND TEXTILES.

GOLDFISH

CHINA MEANS "THE CENTER."

BICYCLES ARE THE MAIN FORM OF TRANSPORTATION.

MILLET

HONG KONG IS A 403-SQUARE-MILE FORMER BRITISH COLONY THAT RETURNED TO CHINESE CONTROL IN 1997.

LIMESTONE HILLS

PIGS

YAMS

SILK

EAST CHINA SEA

THIS RIVER, 2,432 MILES LONG, IS THE THIRD LONGEST IN THE WORLD.

RICE

TAIPEI

TAIWAN IS ONE LARGE ISLAND, PLUS 86 SMALL ONES.

THAT'S A GIBBON.

SUGARCANE

OUR LANGUAGES ARE ENGLISH AND CHINESE.

TAIWAN

I'M A JUNK.

YANGTZE JIANG RIVER

OUR POPULATION IS 22,500,000.

BUDDHISM AND TAOISM ARE PRACTICED.

HONG KONG

WE SPEAK MANDARIN CHINESE AND VARIOUS DIALECTS.

RUBBER TREES

MACAO

FROM 1951 UNTIL 1999...

HONG KONG HARBOR IS A GREAT PORT.

...MACAO WAS A COLONY OF PORTUGAL.

HONG KONG AND MACAO ARE SPECIAL ADMINISTRATIVE DISTRICTS OF CHINA.

NORTH

EAST

WEST

SOUTH

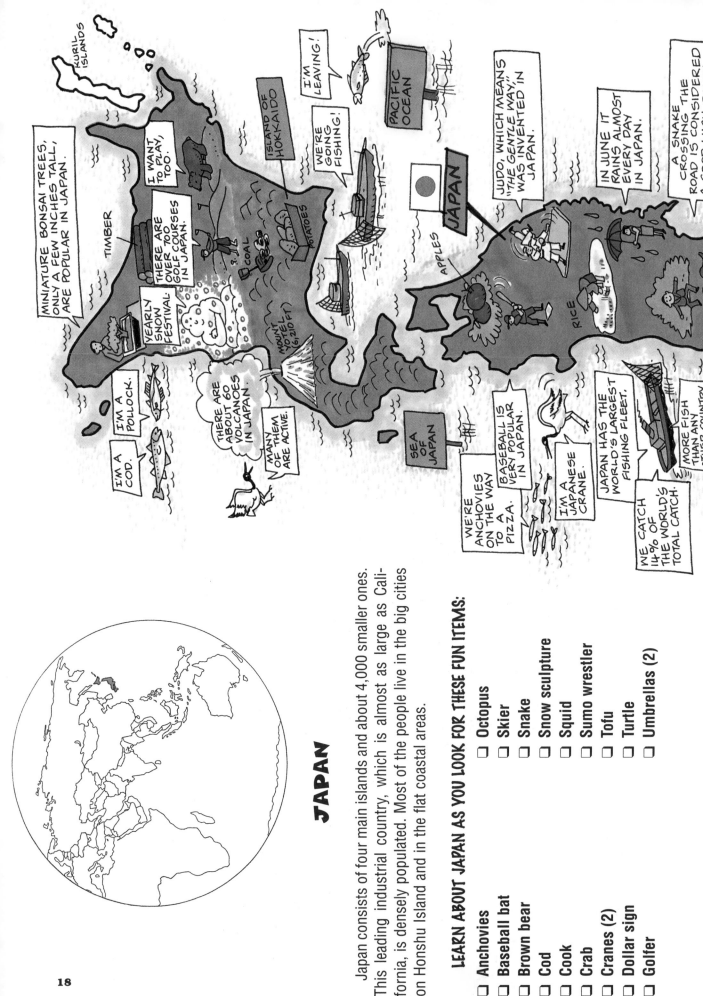

JAPAN

Japan consists of four main islands and about 4,000 smaller ones. This leading industrial country, which is almost as large as California, is densely populated. Most of the people live in the big cities on Honshu Island and in the flat coastal areas.

LEARN ABOUT JAPAN AS YOU LOOK FOR THESE FUN ITEMS:

- ☐ Anchovies
- ☐ Baseball bat
- ☐ Brown bear
- ☐ Cod
- ☐ Cook
- ☐ Crab
- ☐ Cranes (2)
- ☐ Dollar sign
- ☐ Golfer
- ☐ Octopus
- ☐ Skier
- ☐ Snake
- ☐ Snow sculpture
- ☐ Squid
- ☐ Sumo wrestler
- ☐ Tofu
- ☐ Turtle
- ☐ Umbrellas (2)

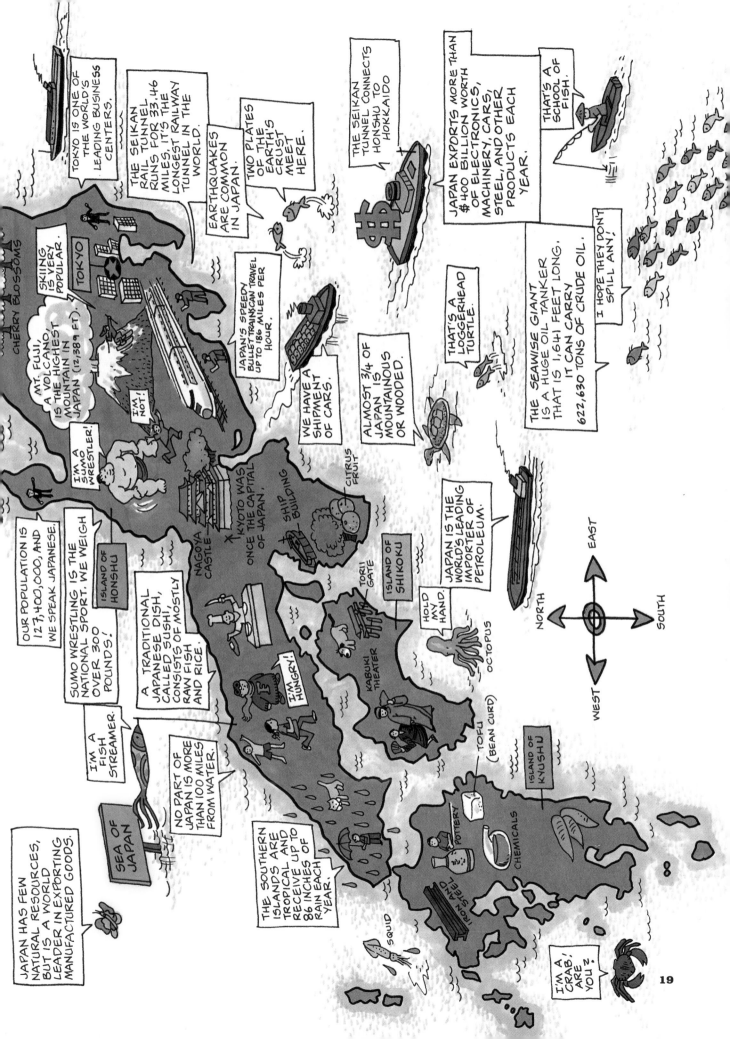

19

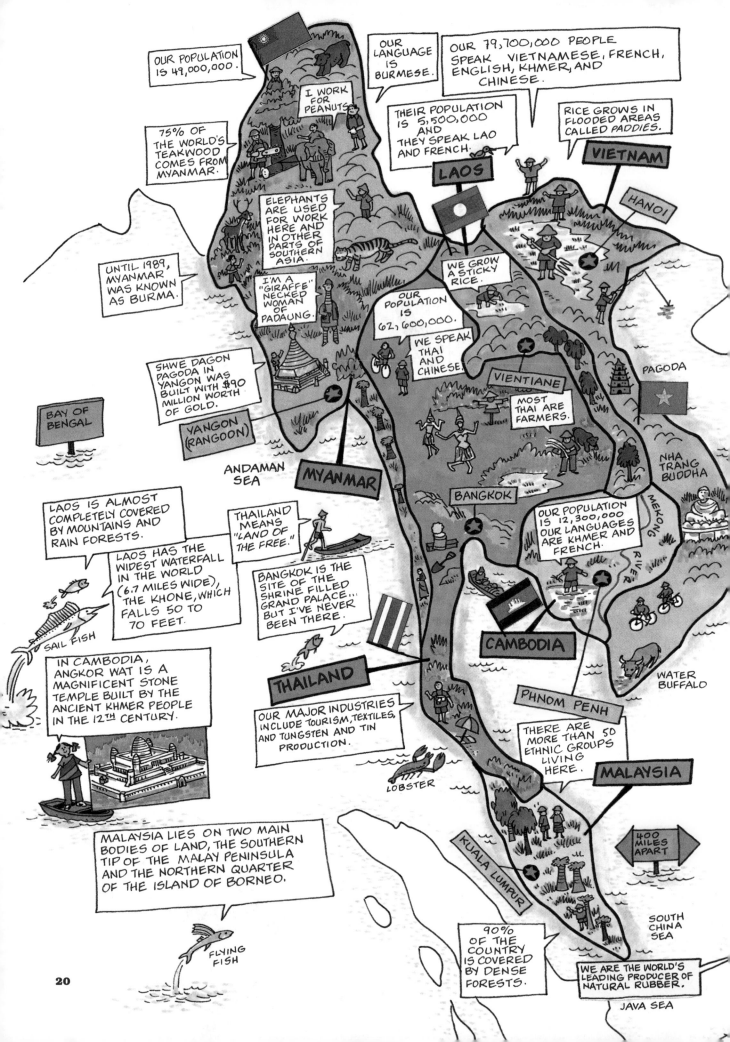

SOUTHEAST ASIA

This region is close to the equator, giving it a tropical climate with periods of heavy rainfall. Dense jungles or tropical rain forests cover much of the area, which has three main types of landscape: mountains, plains, or high, flat areas called plateaus. Most people here live near water—oceans, seas, or mighty rivers. Many Southeast Asians use the waterways for irrigating farmland, fishing, and transportation.

LEARN ABOUT SOUTHEAST ASIA AS YOU LOOK FOR THESE FUN ITEMS:

- ❑ Brown bears (2)
- ❑ Cyclists (3)
- ❑ Dancers
- ❑ Deer
- ❑ Elephant
- ❑ Fisherman
- ❑ Flying fish
- ❑ "Giraffe" necked woman
- ❑ Lobster
- ❑ Pitchfork
- ❑ Scarecrow
- ❑ Tiger
- ❑ Umbrellas (2)

MORE THAN 60% OF THE VIETNAMESE FARM OR FISH.

SOUTH CHINA SEA

VIETNAM HAS A VERY TROPICAL CLIMATE.

DURING THE MONSOON SEASON, STRONG WINDS AND HEAVY RAINS ARE COMMON, ESPECIALLY IN THE SOUTHERN REGIONS.

THEY HAVE ONLY TWO SEASONS- A WET, HOT SUMMER AND A COOL WINTER.

THE HEART OF CAMBODIA IS THE RIVER BASIN WATERED BY THE MEKONG RIVER.

THE MEKONG RIVER CREATES FERTILE FARMING AREAS WHERE MAINLY RICE AND CORN ARE GROWN.

MALAYSIA

BANDAR SERI BEGAWAN

NORTH
WEST EAST
SOUTH

WE MAKE A BEAUTIFUL HANDWOVEN CLOTH WITH GOLD AND SILVER THREADS.

THE POPULATION OF BRUNEI IS 400,000. THEY SPEAK MALAY, CHINESE AND ENGLISH.

BRUNEI

BATIK IS A WAY OF PRINTING FABRIC HERE.

THE WORLD'S LARGEST CAVE CHAMBER IS IN SARAWAK, MALAYSIA. IT'S LARGE ENOUGH TO HOLD ABOUT 7,500 BUSES.

THE POPULATION OF MALAYSIA IS 24,400,000 AND THEY SPEAK BAHASA MALAYSIA AND OTHER LANGUAGES.

BORNEO

ARE WE THERE, YET?

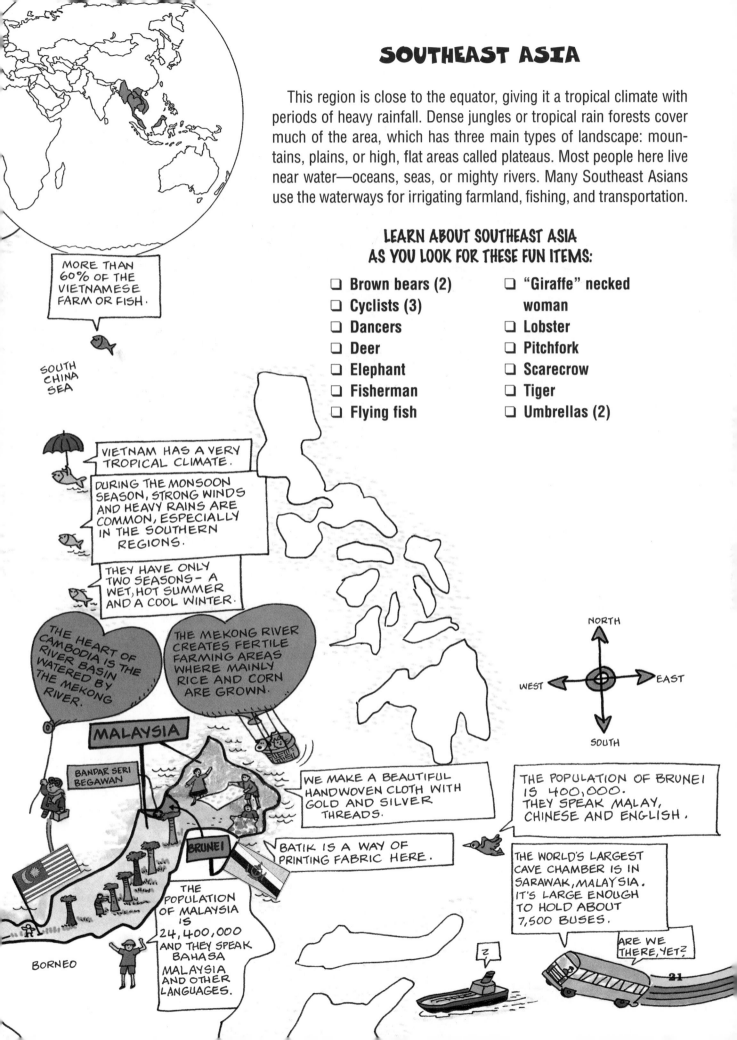

21

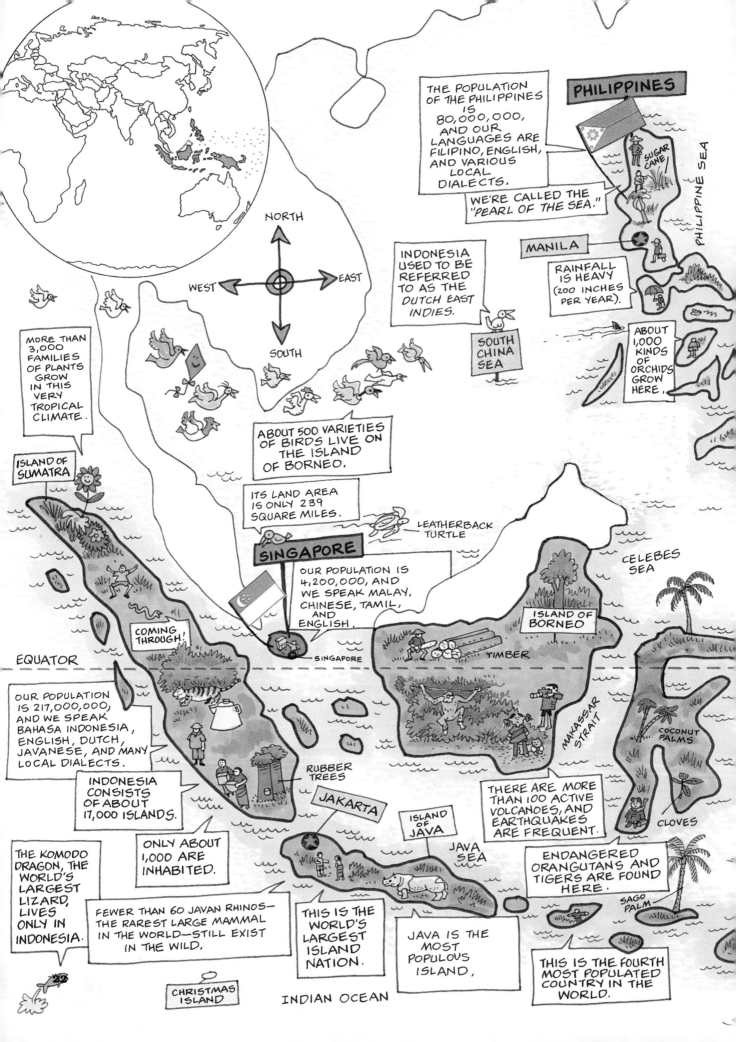

THE POPULATION OF THE PHILIPPINES IS 80,000,000, AND OUR LANGUAGES ARE FILIPINO, ENGLISH, AND VARIOUS LOCAL DIALECTS.

PHILIPPINES

SUGAR CANE

WE'RE CALLED THE "PEARL OF THE SEA."

INDONESIA USED TO BE REFERRED TO AS THE DUTCH EAST INDIES.

MANILA

RAINFALL IS HEAVY (200 INCHES PER YEAR).

PHILIPPINE SEA

SOUTH CHINA SEA

ABOUT 1,000 KINDS OF ORCHIDS GROW HERE.

NORTH
WEST — EAST
SOUTH

MORE THAN 3,000 FAMILIES OF PLANTS GROW IN THIS VERY TROPICAL CLIMATE.

ABOUT 500 VARIETIES OF BIRDS LIVE ON THE ISLAND OF BORNEO.

ISLAND OF SUMATRA

ITS LAND AREA IS ONLY 239 SQUARE MILES.

LEATHERBACK TURTLE

CELEBES SEA

SINGAPORE

OUR POPULATION IS 4,200,000, AND WE SPEAK MALAY, CHINESE, TAMIL, AND ENGLISH.

ISLAND OF BORNEO

COMING THROUGH!

SINGAPORE

TIMBER

MAKASSAR STRAIT

EQUATOR

COCONUT PALMS

OUR POPULATION IS 217,000,000, AND WE SPEAK BAHASA INDONESIA, ENGLISH, DUTCH, JAVANESE, AND MANY LOCAL DIALECTS.

INDONESIA CONSISTS OF ABOUT 17,000 ISLANDS.

RUBBER TREES

JAKARTA

THERE ARE MORE THAN 100 ACTIVE VOLCANOES, AND EARTHQUAKES ARE FREQUENT.

CLOVES

THE KOMODO DRAGON, THE WORLD'S LARGEST LIZARD, LIVES ONLY IN INDONESIA.

ONLY ABOUT 1,000 ARE INHABITED.

ISLAND OF JAVA

JAVA SEA

ENDANGERED ORANGUTANS AND TIGERS ARE FOUND HERE.

SAGO PALM

22

FEWER THAN 60 JAVAN RHINOS— THE RAREST LARGE MAMMAL IN THE WORLD—STILL EXIST IN THE WILD.

THIS IS THE WORLD'S LARGEST ISLAND NATION.

JAVA IS THE MOST POPULOUS ISLAND.

THIS IS THE FOURTH MOST POPULATED COUNTRY IN THE WORLD.

CHRISTMAS ISLAND

INDIAN OCEAN

INDONESIA and PACIFIC ISLAND NATIONS

Indonesia, Singapore, the Philippines, and East Timor are part of Asia. Papua New Guinea and many small island nations scattered in this area of the Pacific Ocean are part of a region called Oceania. *(See p. 5 for a list of all the countries of Oceania.)* Most of this area has a hot, wet, tropical climate.

LEARN ABOUT INDONESIA AND PACIFIC ISLAND NATIONS AS YOU LOOK FOR THESE FUN ITEMS:

❑ Airplane ❑ Orangutan ❑ Shark fins (4) ❑ Turtle
❑ Coffeepot ❑ Photographer ❑ Tiger ❑ Tuna
❑ Kite ❑ Rhinoceros ❑ Tree kangaroo ❑ Volcanoes (2)

THE CLIMATE IS HOT AND HUMID.

OVER 80° IS THE AVERAGE TEMPERATURE.

THERE ARE OVER 7,000 ISLANDS IN THE PHILIPPINES, MOST OF THE PEOPLE LIVE ON THESE 11 ISLANDS.

BONIN ISLANDS (JAPAN)

OF ABOUT 25,000 ISLANDS IN THE PACIFIC OCEAN, ONLY A FEW THOUSAND ARE INHABITED.

NORTHERN MARIANA ISLANDS (U.S.)

WAKE ISLAND (U.S.)

NORTH PACIFIC OCEAN

PALAU

SOME OF THE PACIFIC ISLANDS MAKE UP NINE INDEPENDENT COUNTRIES.

MARSHALL ISLANDS

MANY OTHER ISLANDS ARE GOVERNED BY COUNTRIES SUCH AS THE U.S., GREAT BRITAIN, AND FRANCE.

VOLCANIC ERUPTIONS ARE COMMON. THESE ISLANDS ARE ACTUALLY THE TOPS OF MOUNTAINS THAT ARE STILL FORMING.

MICRONESIA

SOME OF THE ISLANDS ARE THE TIPS OF MOUNTAINS OR VOLCANOES, OTHERS ARE MADE UP OF CORAL.

I'M A PEARL OYSTER.

KIRIBATI

EQUATOR

PAPUA NEW GUINEA

OUR POPULATION IS 5,000,000, AND OUR LANGUAGES ARE ENGLISH, PIDGIN ENGLISH, MOTU, AND MANY OTHERS.

MOLUCCA SEA

INDONESIA

HALF THE ISLAND BELONGS TO INDONESIA.

RAINFALL IS OVER 100 INCHES ANNUALLY.

BISMARCK SEA

MT. WILHELM (14,790 FT)

TREE KANGAROO

BANDA SEA

INDONESIA'S MAIN EXPORTS ARE OIL, TIMBER, RUBBER AND COFFEE.

TUVALU

SOLOMON ISLANDS

DILI

EAST TIMOR

EAST TIMOR'S LANGUAGES ARE TETUM, PORTUGUESE, INDONESIAN, ENGLISH, AND OTHERS.

EAST TIMOR— THE WORLD'S NEWEST COUNTRY —BECAME INDEPENDENT IN 2002.

PORT MORESBY

VANUATU

FIJI

EAST TIMOR'S POPULATION IS 800,000.

ARAFURA SEA

CORAL SEA IS. (AUS.)

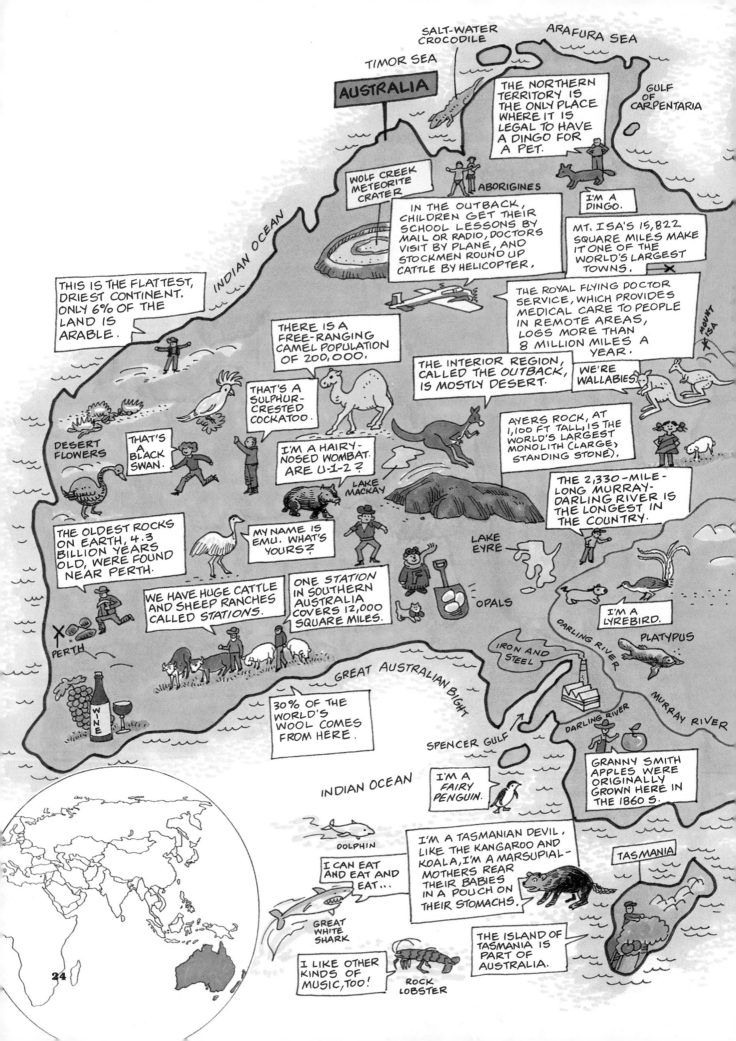

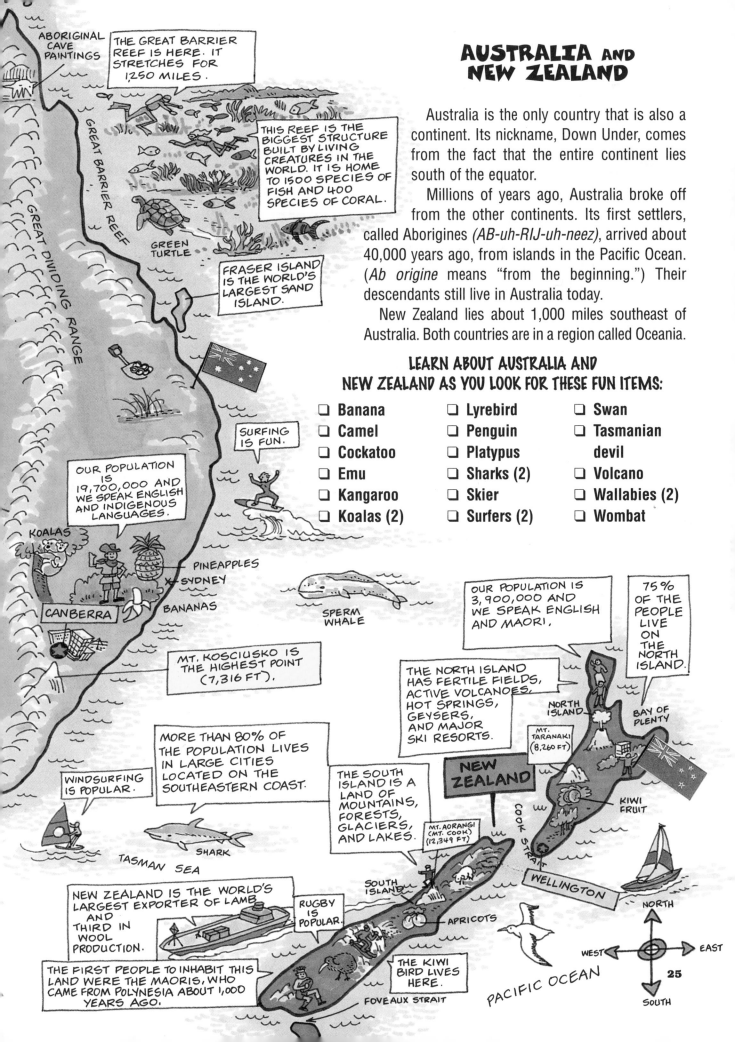

AUSTRALIA AND NEW ZEALAND

Australia is the only country that is also a continent. Its nickname, Down Under, comes from the fact that the entire continent lies south of the equator.

Millions of years ago, Australia broke off from the other continents. Its first settlers, called Aborigines *(AB-uh-RIJ-uh-neez)*, arrived about 40,000 years ago, from islands in the Pacific Ocean. (*Ab origine* means "from the beginning.") Their descendants still live in Australia today.

New Zealand lies about 1,000 miles southeast of Australia. Both countries are in a region called Oceania.

LEARN ABOUT AUSTRALIA AND NEW ZEALAND AS YOU LOOK FOR THESE FUN ITEMS:

- ❏ Banana
- ❏ Camel
- ❏ Cockatoo
- ❏ Emu
- ❏ Kangaroo
- ❏ Koalas (2)
- ❏ Lyrebird
- ❏ Penguin
- ❏ Platypus
- ❏ Sharks (2)
- ❏ Skier
- ❏ Surfers (2)
- ❏ Swan
- ❏ Tasmanian devil
- ❏ Volcano
- ❏ Wallabies (2)
- ❏ Wombat

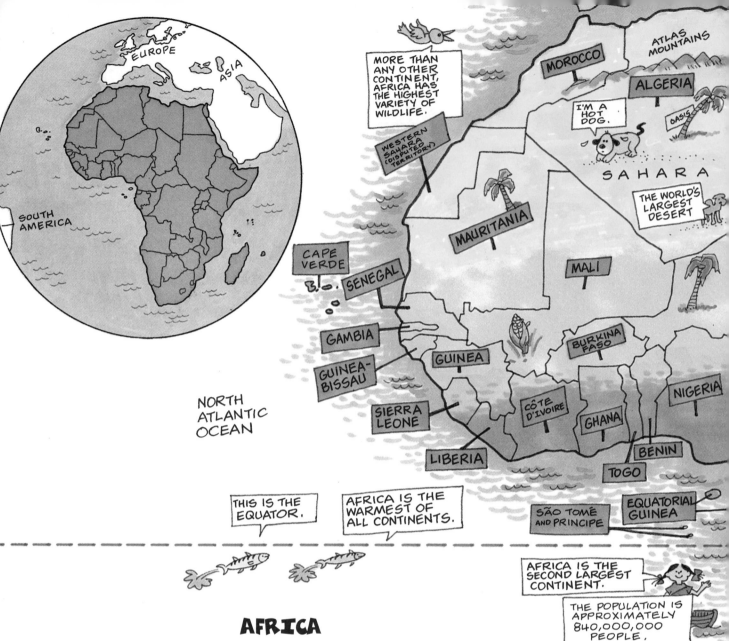

AFRICA

Once an unexplored and mysterious place to Europeans, Africa was known as the "Dark Continent." By the 19th century, European powers influenced or controlled much of Africa. However, starting in the late 1950s, country after country in Africa achieved its independence. The continent now is home to 53 independent nations. Africa's newest country, Eritrea, became independent in 1993, when it split from Ethiopia.

LEARN ABOUT AFRICA AS YOU LOOK FOR THESE FUN ITEMS:

- ☐ Atlas Mountains
- ☐ Butterfly
- ☐ Cape of Good Hope
- ☐ Elephant
- ☐ Gold bar
- ☐ Indian Ocean

- ☐ Mount Kilimanjaro
- ☐ Nile River
- ☐ Oil wells (2)
- ☐ Palm trees (4)
- ☐ Pyramid
- ☐ Rain cloud

- ☐ Rhinoceros
- ☐ Sea horse
- ☐ Sheep (2)
- ☐ Suez Canal
- ☐ Umbrella
- ☐ Zebra

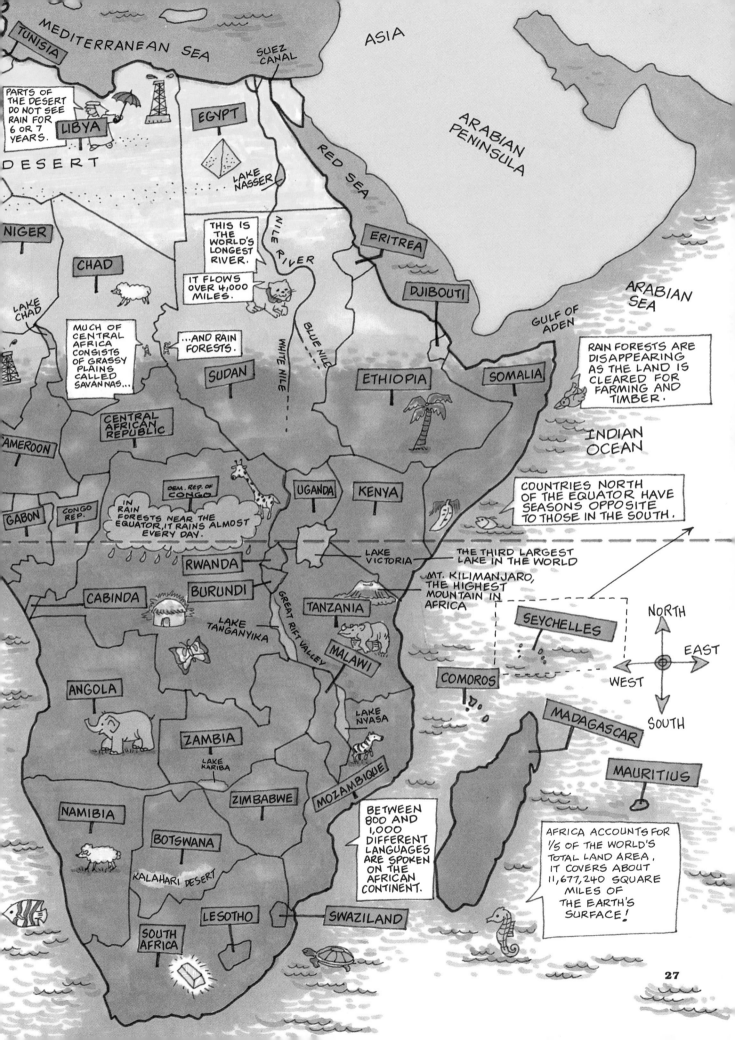

TUNISIA

MEDITERRANEAN SEA

ASIA

SUEZ CANAL

PARTS OF THE DESERT DO NOT SEE RAIN FOR 6 OR 7 YEARS.

LIBYA

EGYPT

ARABIAN PENINSULA

DESERT

LAKE NASSER

RED SEA

NIGER

CHAD

THIS IS THE WORLD'S LONGEST RIVER.

NILE RIVER

ERITREA

ARABIAN SEA

LAKE CHAD

IT FLOWS OVER 4,000 MILES.

DJIBOUTI

GULF OF ADEN

MUCH OF CENTRAL AFRICA CONSISTS OF GRASSY PLAINS CALLED SAVANNAS...

...AND RAIN FORESTS.

WHITE NILE

BLUE NILE

SUDAN

ETHIOPIA

SOMALIA

RAIN FORESTS ARE DISAPPEARING AS THE LAND IS CLEARED FOR FARMING AND TIMBER.

CAMEROON

CENTRAL AFRICAN REPUBLIC

INDIAN OCEAN

DEM. REP. OF CONGO

UGANDA

KENYA

COUNTRIES NORTH OF THE EQUATOR HAVE SEASONS OPPOSITE TO THOSE IN THE SOUTH.

GABON

CONGO REP.

IN RAIN FORESTS NEAR THE EQUATOR, IT RAINS ALMOST EVERY DAY.

LAKE VICTORIA

THE THIRD LARGEST LAKE IN THE WORLD

RWANDA

BURUNDI

MT. KILIMANJARO, THE HIGHEST MOUNTAIN IN AFRICA

NORTH

CABINDA

GREAT RIFT VALLEY

LAKE TANGANYIKA

TANZANIA

SEYCHELLES

EAST

MALAWI

COMOROS

WEST

ANGOLA

LAKE NYASA

MADAGASCAR

SOUTH

ZAMBIA

LAKE KARIBA

MAURITIUS

NAMIBIA

ZIMBABWE

MOZAMBIQUE

BOTSWANA

BETWEEN 800 AND 1,000 DIFFERENT LANGUAGES ARE SPOKEN ON THE AFRICAN CONTINENT.

AFRICA ACCOUNTS FOR 1/5 OF THE WORLD'S TOTAL LAND AREA, IT COVERS ABOUT 11,677,240 SQUARE MILES OF THE EARTH'S SURFACE!

KALAHARI DESERT

LESOTHO

SWAZILAND

SOUTH AFRICA

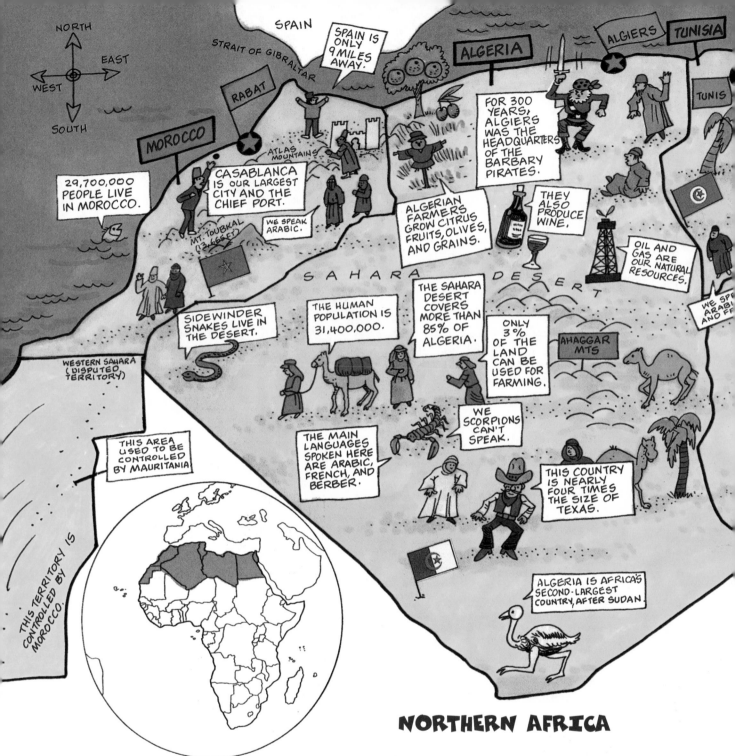

NORTHERN AFRICA

The peoples of ancient Greece, Rome, and Arabia influenced cultures in this part of Africa, and African culture—especially that of ancient Egypt—influenced them. In northern Africa today, Arabic is the dominant language and Islam is the major religion. Although Egypt is on the African continent, politically it often is considered part of the region known as the Middle East.

LEARN ABOUT NORTHERN AFRICA AS YOU LOOK FOR THESE FUN ITEMS:

- ☐ Barbary ape
- ☐ Beret
- ☐ Boats (3)
- ☐ Bunch of grapes
- ☐ Hyena
- ☐ Miner
- ☐ Mummy
- ☐ Orange tree
- ☐ Oil wells (4)
- ☐ Ostrich
- ☐ Palm trees (3)
- ☐ Pencil
- ☐ Pirate
- ☐ Pyramids (4)
- ☐ Scarecrow
- ☐ Scorpion
- ☐ Shovel
- ☐ Snake
- ☐ Thermometer

THE SAHEL

Just south of the Sahara Desert is a region called the Sahel, long inhabited by animal grazers and farmers. Much of the area is changing into desert as the Sahara expands southward at a rate of about three miles a year.

LEARN ABOUT THE SAHEL AS YOU LOOK FOR THESE FUN ITEMS:

- ❑ Anchor
- ❑ Basket
- ❑ Bird
- ❑ Camels (5)
- ❑ Cotton balls (3)
- ❑ Goat
- ❑ Elephant
- ❑ Fisherman
- ❑ Hippopotamus
- ❑ Lake Chad
- ❑ Niger River
- ❑ Peanuts (3)
- ❑ Periscope
- ❑ Soccer ball
- ❑ Sun
- ❑ Tent

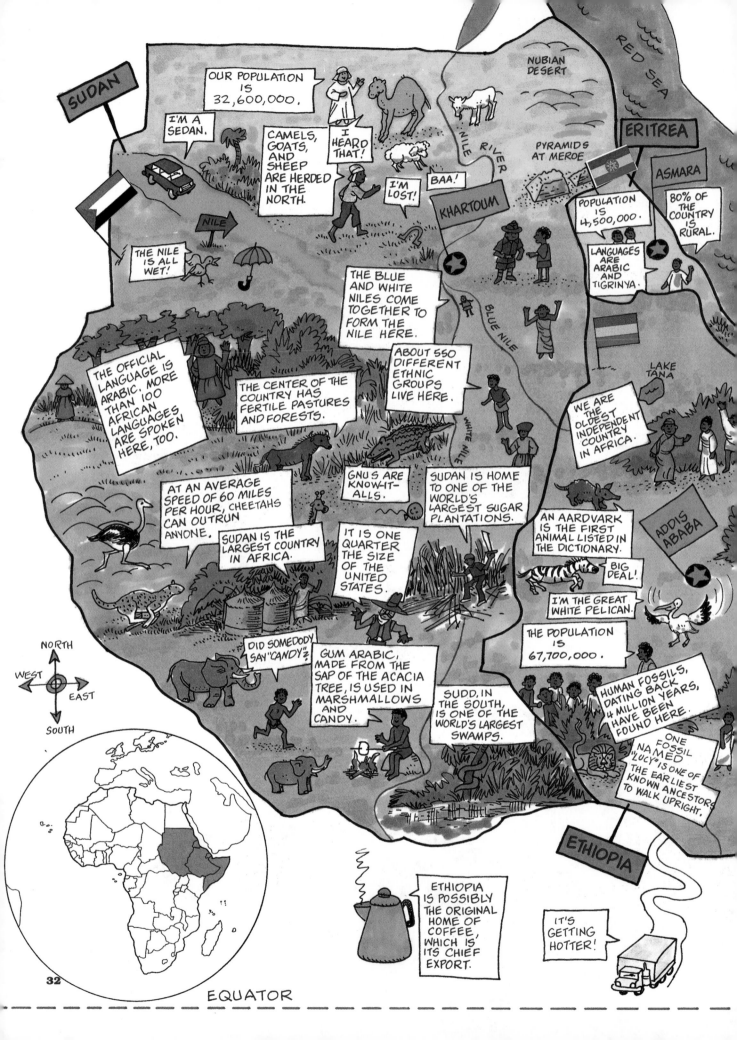

THE HORN OF AFRICA

The region along Africa's northeastern coast is known as the Horn of Africa. On maps, its shape looks like the horn of a rhinoceros jutting into the Indian Ocean.

LEARN ABOUT THE HORN OF AFRICA AS YOU LOOK FOR THESE FUN ITEMS:

- ❏ Aardvark
- ❏ Acacia tree
- ❏ Banana
- ❏ Coffeepot
- ❏ Cotton
- ❏ Giraffes (2)
- ❏ Horseshoe
- ❏ Lion
- ❏ Marshmallow
- ❏ Nile crocodile
- ❏ Nubian Desert
- ❏ Oryx
- ❏ Ostrich
- ❏ Red Sea
- ❏ Umbrella
- ❏ White Nile
- ❏ Zebra

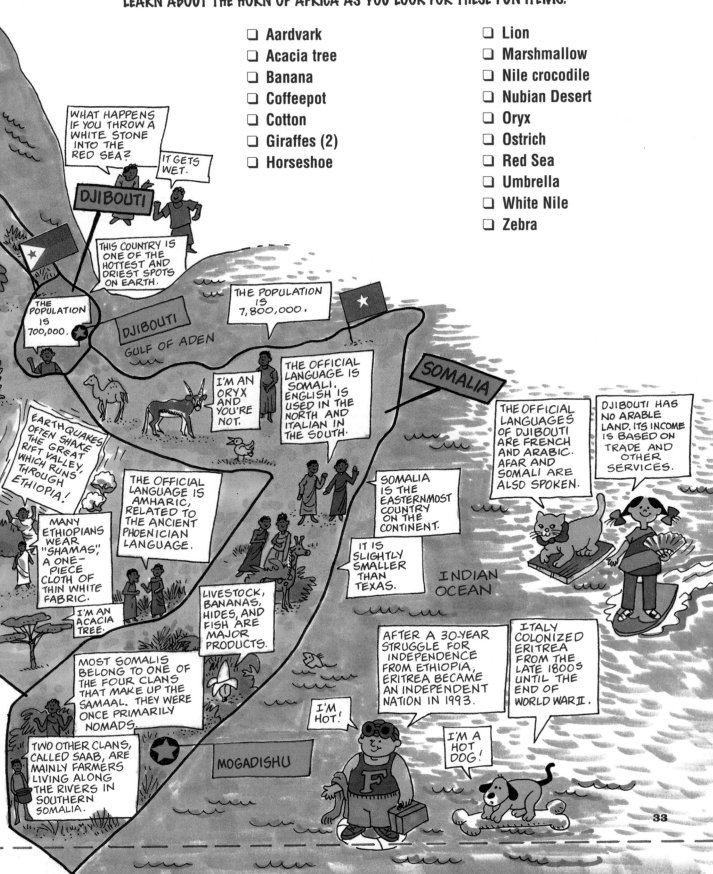

WHAT HAPPENS IF YOU THROW A WHITE STONE INTO THE RED SEA?

IT GETS WET.

DJIBOUTI

THIS COUNTRY IS ONE OF THE HOTTEST AND DRIEST SPOTS ON EARTH.

THE POPULATION IS 700,000.

DJIBOUTI

GULF OF ADEN

THE POPULATION IS 7,800,000.

I'M AN ORYX AND YOU'RE NOT.

THE OFFICIAL LANGUAGE IS SOMALI. ENGLISH IS USED IN THE NORTH AND ITALIAN IN THE SOUTH.

SOMALIA

THE OFFICIAL LANGUAGES OF DJIBOUTI ARE FRENCH AND ARABIC. AFAR AND SOMALI ARE ALSO SPOKEN.

DJIBOUTI HAS NO ARABLE LAND. ITS INCOME IS BASED ON TRADE AND OTHER SERVICES.

EARTHQUAKES OFTEN SHAKE THE GREAT RIFT VALLEY, WHICH RUNS THROUGH ETHIOPIA!

THE OFFICIAL LANGUAGE IS AMHARIC, RELATED TO THE ANCIENT PHOENICIAN LANGUAGE.

SOMALIA IS THE EASTERNMOST COUNTRY ON THE CONTINENT.

MANY ETHIOPIANS WEAR "SHAMAS", A ONE-PIECE CLOTH OF THIN WHITE FABRIC.

IT IS SLIGHTLY SMALLER THAN TEXAS.

I'M AN ACACIA TREE.

LIVESTOCK, BANANAS, HIDES, AND FISH ARE MAJOR PRODUCTS.

INDIAN OCEAN

MOST SOMALIS BELONG TO ONE OF THE FOUR CLANS THAT MAKE UP THE SAMAAL. THEY WERE ONCE PRIMARILY NOMADS.

AFTER A 30-YEAR STRUGGLE FOR INDEPENDENCE FROM ETHIOPIA, ERITREA BECAME AN INDEPENDENT NATION IN 1993.

ITALY COLONIZED ERITREA FROM THE LATE 1800S UNTIL THE END OF WORLD WAR II.

TWO OTHER CLANS, CALLED SAAB, ARE MAINLY FARMERS LIVING ALONG THE RIVERS IN SOUTHERN SOMALIA.

I'M HOT!

MOGADISHU

I'M A HOT DOG!

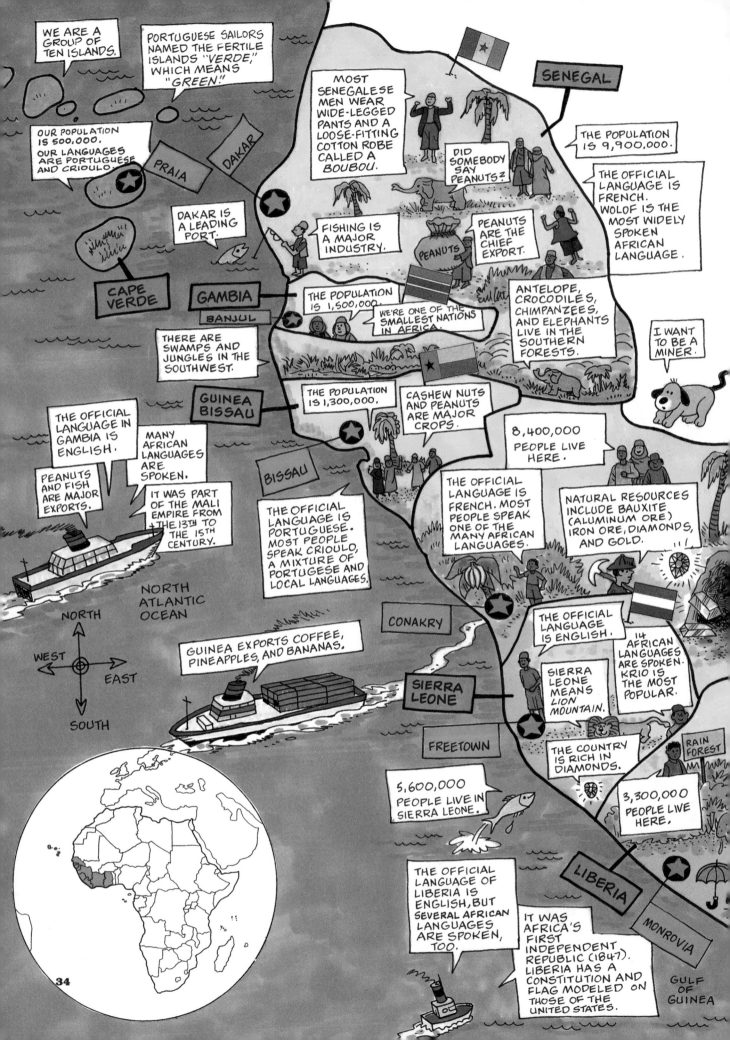

THE UPPER WEST COAST

Africa's upper west coast—the part that, seen on a map, bulges out into the Atlantic Ocean—has a landscape that varies from humid coastal plains and swamps to forested hills and plateaus. The soil is fertile, and farmers in this area grow such crops as cocoa, coffee, and peanuts.

During the era of the slave trade to the Americas, and for centuries before with other nations, coastal kingdoms of West Africa grew rich by trading slaves, gold, and ivory with Europeans.

LEARN ABOUT AFRICA'S UPPER WEST COAST AS YOU LOOK FOR THESE FUN ITEMS:

- ❑ Boats (4)
- ❑ Chocolate bar
- ❑ Coffeepot
- ❑ Crocodile
- ❑ Diamonds (4)
- ❑ Elephants
- ❑ Fishermen
- ❑ Game warden
- ❑ Gold bars (3)
- ❑ Lake Volta
- ❑ Lion
- ❑ Miner
- ❑ Pygmy hippopotamus
- ❑ Rain clouds (2)
- ❑ Umbrella

GUINEA

I'D LIKE A CHOCOLATE BAR.

I LOVE PEANUTS.

GHANA

I SEE A CUTE LION.

CÔTE D'IVOIRE

THE POPULATION IS 20,200,000.

THE OFFICIAL LANGUAGE IS ENGLISH, BUT THERE ARE MANY AFRICAN LANGUAGES SPOKEN HERE.

HISTORY IS RECITED BY STORYTELLERS CALLED GRIOTS.

THE POPULATION IS 16,800,000.

WE EXPORT COFFEE, COCOA, AND TROPICAL WOODS.

COCOA BEANS

THE OFFICIAL LANGUAGE IS FRENCH. AFRICAN LANGUAGES INCLUDE DIOULA, BAOULE, AND BETE.

BEFORE GAINING INDEPENDENCE FROM GREAT BRITAIN IN 1957, GHANA USED TO BE KNOWN AS THE GOLD COAST.

THE COUNTRY WAS NAMED FOR THE IVORY TRADE, WHICH FLOURISHED FROM THE 13TH TO EARLY 20TH CENTURY.

YAMOUSSOUKRO

RAIN FOREST

LAKE VOLTA

AN ENDANGERED SPECIES, THE PYGMY HIPPOPOTAMUS LIVES IN THE MARSHY SOUTHERN AREA OF GHANA.

WE EXPORT RUBBER, TIMBER, AND COCOA.

TODAY, IVORY TRADE IS ILLEGAL, AND THE NATION PROTECTS ITS ELEPHANTS IN GAME PRESERVES.

NATURAL RESOURCES INCLUDE GOLD, DIAMONDS, AND FISH.

ACCRA IS A MAJOR HUB FOR ROADS, RAILWAYS, AND SHIPPING.

LIBERIA WAS FOUNDED FOR THE SETTLEMENT OF FREED AMERICAN SLAVES.

NO HUNTING

IT'S SAFE HERE.

CHOCOLATE

COCOA BEANS ARE THE NUMBER-ONE EXPORT.

ACCRA

35

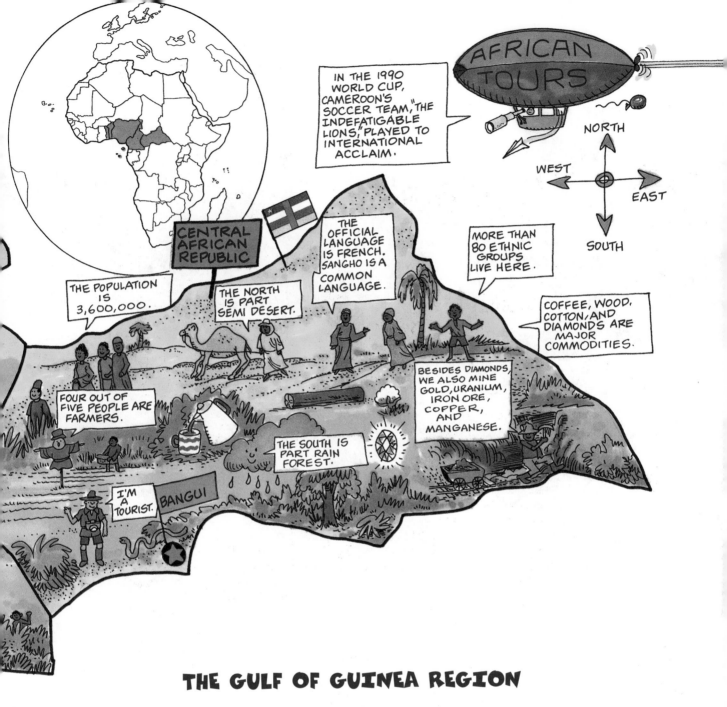

THE GULF OF GUINEA REGION

The Gulf of Guinea is a large section of the Atlantic that lies in the curve of Africa's bulging upper west coast. Many of the countries in this region share the "slave coast" history of the upper west coast countries (pp. 34-35). The gulf region has a richly varied landscape that includes old volcanic mountains, semidesert areas, swamps, tropical rain forests, and savannas. (*Savanna* is tropical or subtropical grassland.)

LEARN ABOUT AFRICA'S GULF OF GUINEA REGION AS YOU LOOK FOR THESE FUN ITEMS:

- ❑ Camera
- ❑ Cup
- ❑ Fishing poles (2)
- ❑ Giraffe
- ❑ Huts (2)

- ❑ Life preserver
- ❑ Oil wells (3)
- ❑ Paper airplane
- ❑ Red car
- ❑ Scarecrow

- ❑ Shark
- ❑ Snakes (2)
- ❑ Telescope
- ❑ Umbrellas
- ❑ Volcano

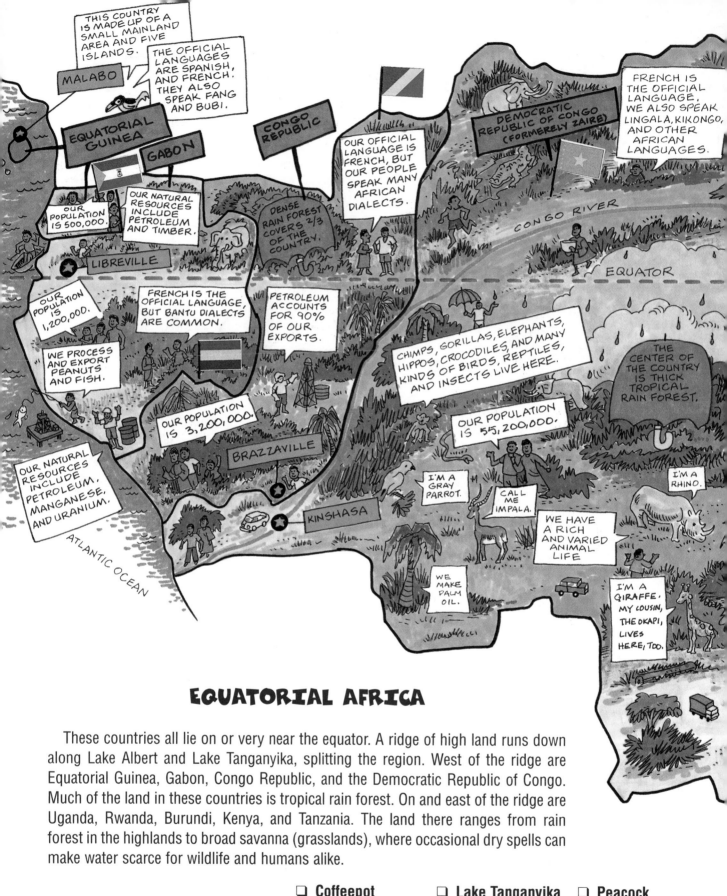

EQUATORIAL AFRICA

These countries all lie on or very near the equator. A ridge of high land runs down along Lake Albert and Lake Tanganyika, splitting the region. West of the ridge are Equatorial Guinea, Gabon, Congo Republic, and the Democratic Republic of Congo. Much of the land in these countries is tropical rain forest. On and east of the ridge are Uganda, Rwanda, Burundi, Kenya, and Tanzania. The land there ranges from rain forest in the highlands to broad savanna (grasslands), where occasional dry spells can make water scarce for wildlife and humans alike.

LEARN ABOUT EQUATORIAL AFRICA AS YOU LOOK FOR THESE FUN ITEMS:

- ❏ Coffeepot
- ❏ Congo River
- ❏ Crocodile
- ❏ Elephants (4)
- ❏ Gorilla
- ❏ Lake Tanganyika
- ❏ Lion
- ❏ Mount Kilimanjaro
- ❏ Parrot
- ❏ Peacock
- ❏ Snake
- ❏ Umbrellas (3)
- ❏ Zanzibar
- ❏ Zebra

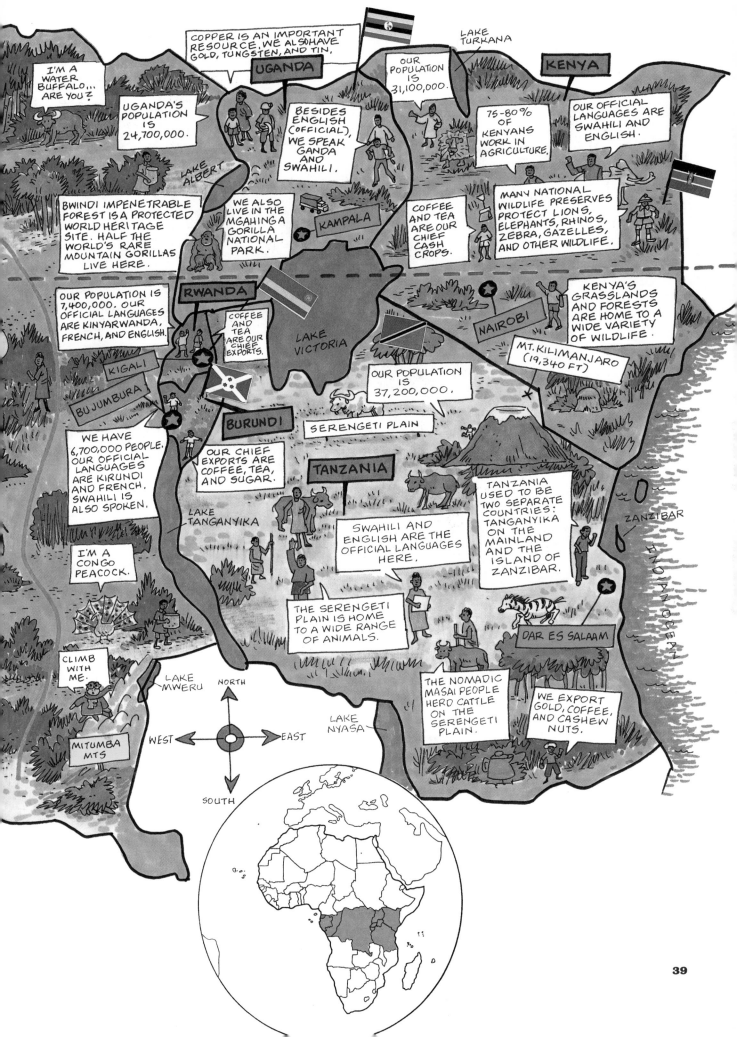

39

ANGOLA, ZAMBIA, MALAWI, AND MOZAMBIQUE

The region that lies south of the equatorial rain forests, between the South Atlantic Ocean and the Indian Ocean, has lots of open savanna and many farms. The area is home to antelope, elephants, giraffes, zebras, and many other animals.

LEARN ABOUT ANGOLA, ZAMBIA, MALAWI, AND MOZAMBIQUE AS YOU LOOK FOR THESE FUN ITEMS:

- ❑ Bananas (2)
- ❑ Cars (2)
- ❑ Coffee cups (2)
- ❑ Cow
- ❑ Eyeglasses
- ❑ Fish (3)
- ❑ Giraffe
- ❑ Hornbill
- ❑ Kariba Dam
- ❑ Leopard
- ❑ Rhinoceros
- ❑ Rice farmer
- ❑ Ring
- ❑ Scarecrow
- ❑ Shovel
- ❑ Snakes (2)
- ❑ Sun
- ❑ Victoria Falls

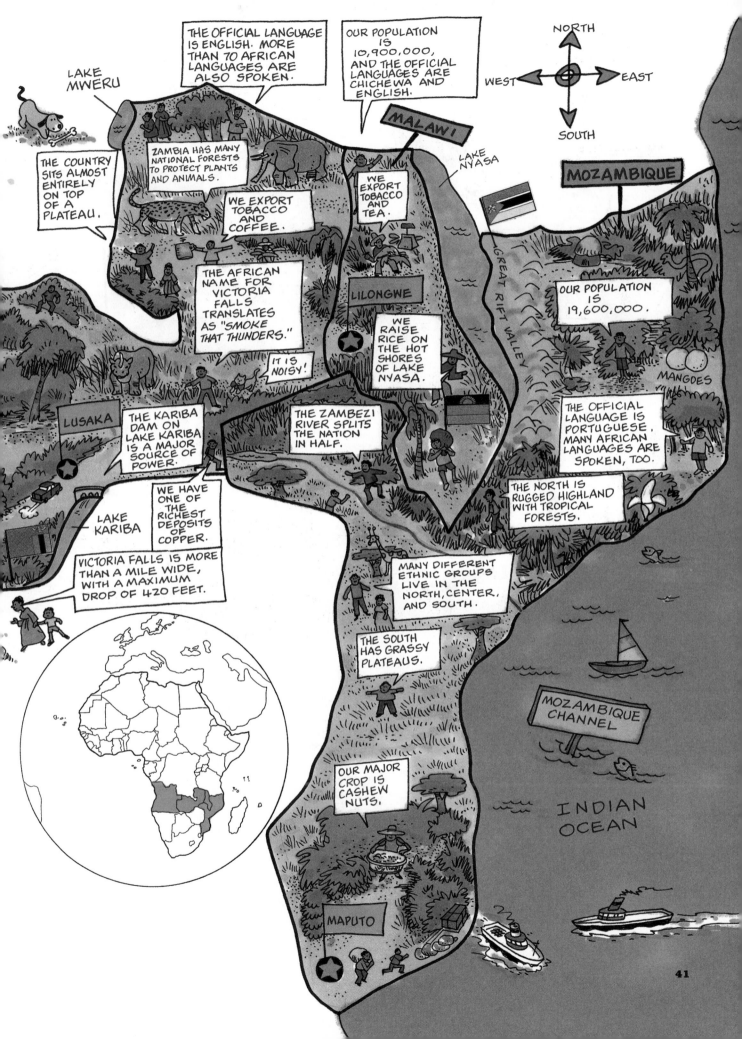

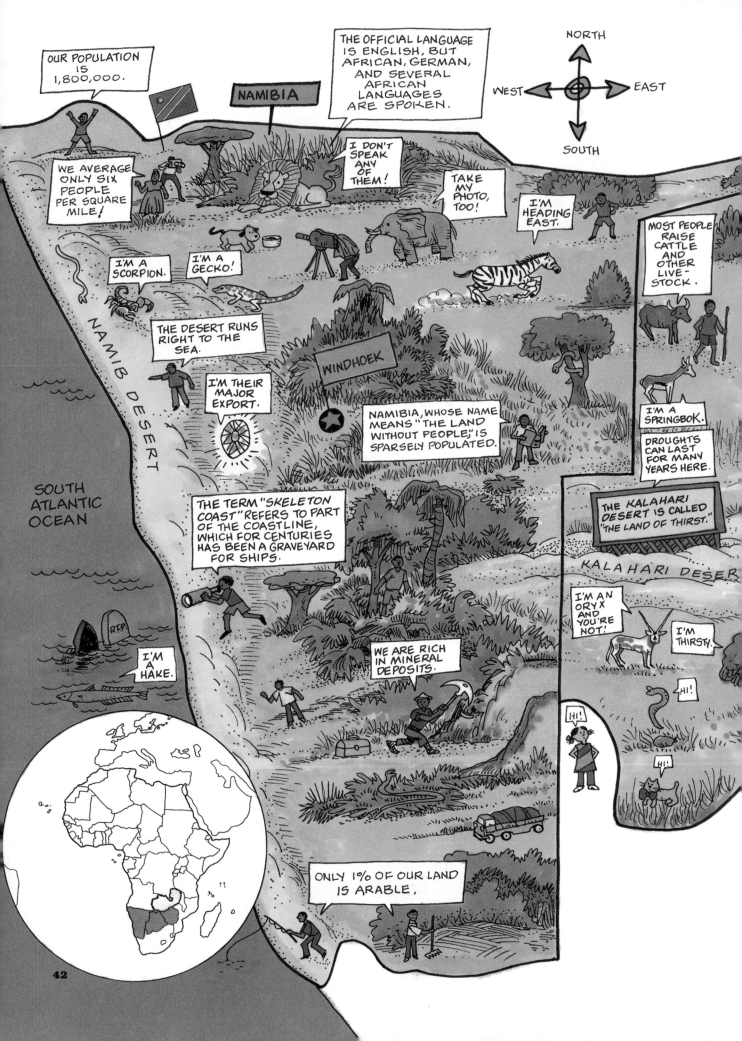

42

NAMIBIA, BOTSWANA, AND ZIMBABWE

Rich deposits of diamonds, gold, and minerals make this area one of the fastest-growing economic regions in Africa. Though rich in natural resources, such as diamonds and minerals, very little of the land in Namibia and Botswana is habitable. Namibia has only six people per square mile and Botswana has only seven. With its more-arable land and better-developed industries, Zimbabwe has 82 people per square mile.

LEARN ABOUT NAMIBIA, BOTSWANA, AND ZIMBABWE AS YOU LOOK FOR THESE FUN ITEMS:

- ☐ Baby
- ☐ Billboard
- ☐ Book
- ☐ Elephants (6)
- ☐ Fishing pole
- ☐ Lions (2)
- ☐ Lost snowman
- ☐ Namib Desert
- ☐ Oryx
- ☐ Picks (2)
- ☐ Rake
- ☐ Scorpion
- ☐ Shipwreck
- ☐ Snakes (5)
- ☐ Sneaker
- ☐ Snowman
- ☐ Truck
- ☐ Zebras (2)

SOUTH AFRICA, LESOTHO, AND SWAZILAND

The world's greatest diamond and gold mines are in South Africa, making it the richest country in Africa. The mines employ tens of thousands of men from neighboring countries.

Lesotho and Swaziland are two small, landlocked countries. One is completely surrounded by South Africa, the other is mostly so. Both are completely dependent on South Africa and Mozambique for trade routes to the ocean and other countries.

LEARN ABOUT SOUTH AFRICA, LESOTHO, AND SWAZILAND AS YOU LOOK FOR THESE FUN ITEMS:

- [ ] Cars (4)
- [ ] Citrus fruit
- [ ] Crown
- [ ] Drummer
- [ ] Giraffes (3)
- [ ] Grapes
- [ ] Guitar
- [ ] Lion
- [ ] Orange River
- [ ] Ostrich
- [ ] Pineapple
- [ ] Sailor
- [ ] Scarecrow
- [ ] Sheep (2)
- [ ] Shovel
- [ ] Table Mountain
- [ ] Tent
- [ ] Tractor
- [ ] Zebra
- [ ] Zulu warrior

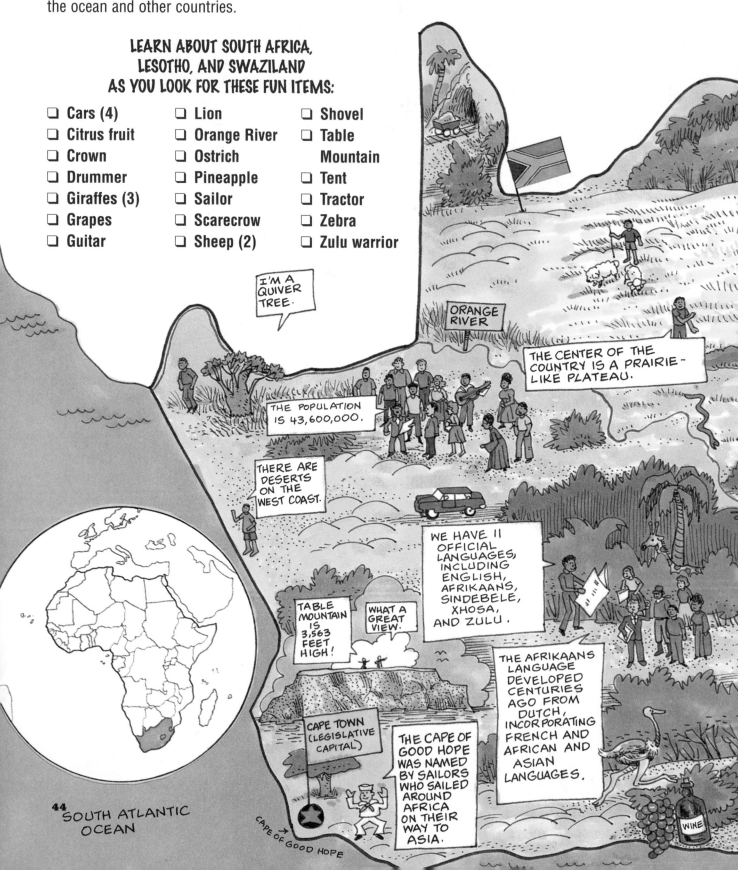

SOUTH ATLANTIC OCEAN

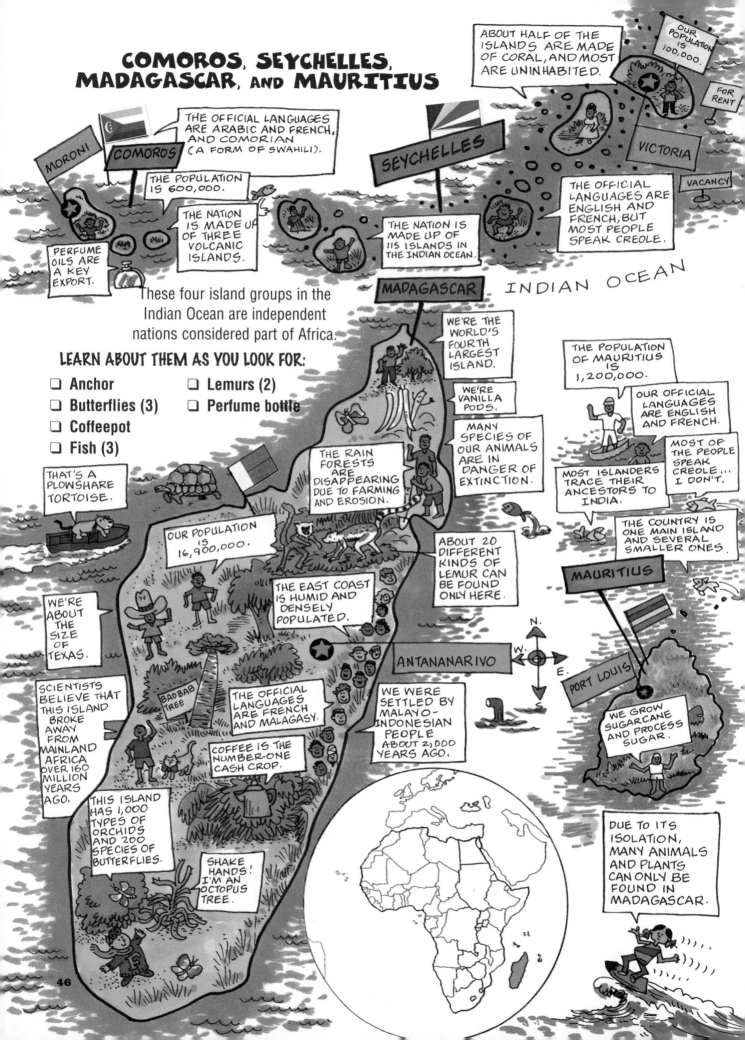

COMOROS, SEYCHELLES, MADAGASCAR, AND MAURITIUS

These four island groups in the Indian Ocean are independent nations considered part of Africa.

LEARN ABOUT THEM AS YOU LOOK FOR:

- ❑ Anchor
- ❑ Butterflies (3)
- ❑ Coffeepot
- ❑ Fish (3)
- ❑ Lemurs (2)
- ❑ Perfume bottle

ANTARCTICA

With temperatures as low as -125° F, this continent is the coldest place on Earth. By international agreement, no one owns the land, and scientific research bases are the only inhabited places.

LEARN ABOUT ANTARCTICA AS YOU LOOK FOR THESE FUN ITEMS:

- ☐ Dinosaur
- ☐ Elephant seals (3)
- ☐ Lost mitten
- ☐ Snowman
- ☐ Snow-mobile

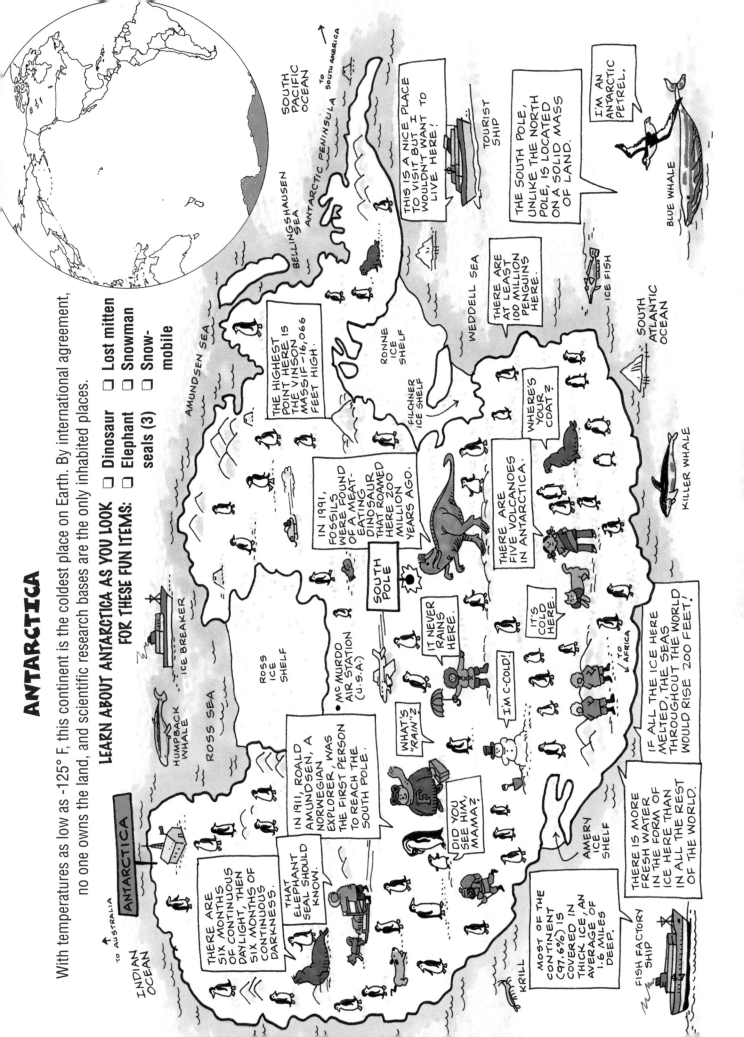

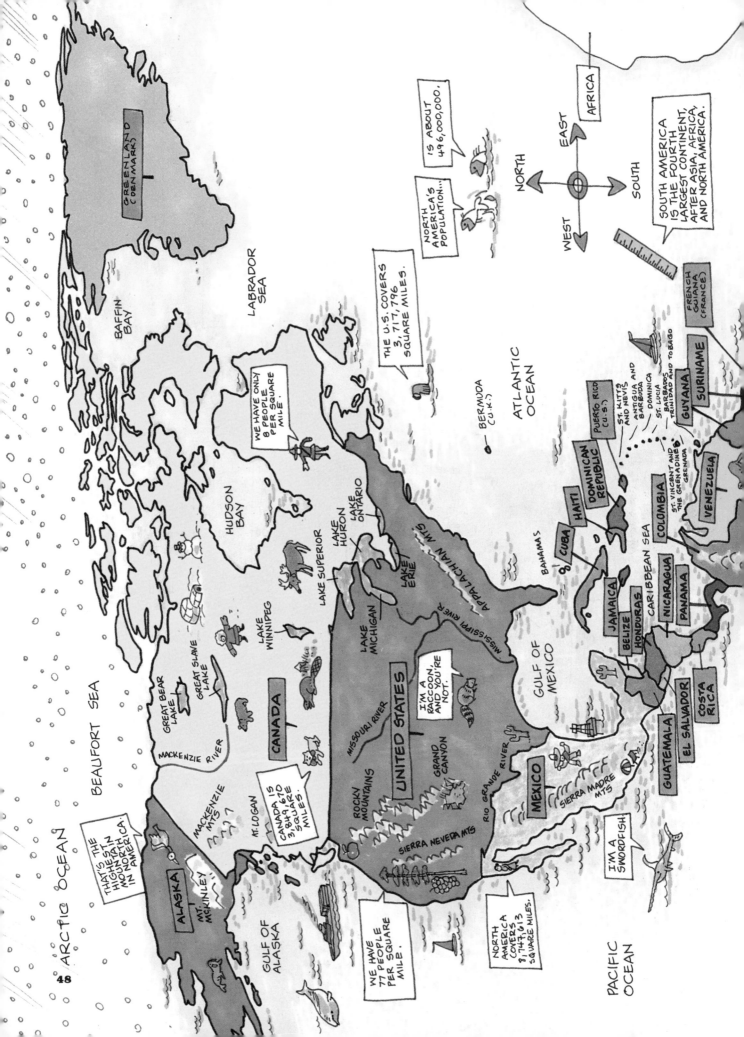

NORTH AMERICA and SOUTH AMERICA

North America is the third largest of the seven continents. It stretches from Greenland and Canada in the Arctic north to Panama, which is near the equator. Islands in the Caribbean Sea are are also part of North America.

South America is the fourth largest continent. From equatorial Colombia, it extends farther south than any continent except Antarctica.

LEARN ABOUT NORTH AND SOUTH AMERICA AS YOU LOOK FOR THESE FUN ITEMS:

- ☐ Banana
- ☐ Cactuses (2)
- ☐ Coffeepot
- ☐ Igloo
- ☐ Monkey
- ☐ Moose
- ☐ Parrot
- ☐ Penguin
- ☐ Periscope
- ☐ Sailboats (2)
- ☐ Shipwreck
- ☐ Snowman
- ☐ Soccer player
- ☐ Surfer
- ☐ Swordfish

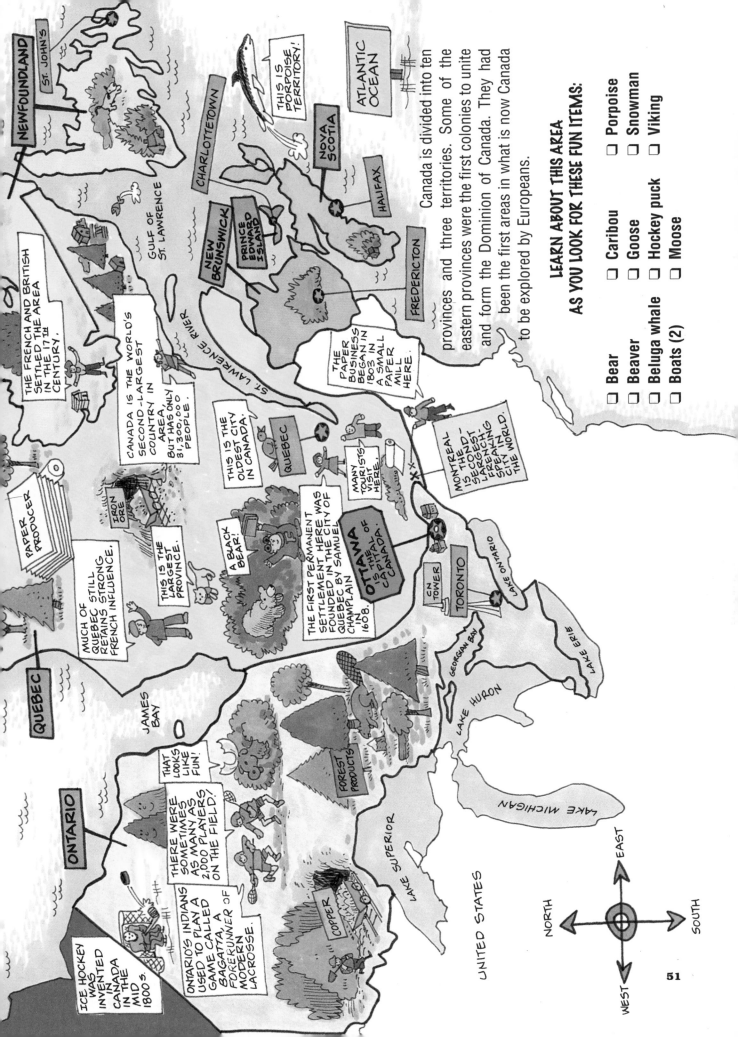

NEWFOUNDLAND

ST. JOHN'S

CHARLOTTETOWN

THIS IS PORPOISE TERRITORY!

ATLANTIC OCEAN

NOVA SCOTIA

HALIFAX

NEW BRUNSWICK

PRINCE EDWARD ISLAND

FREDERICTON

GULF OF ST. LAWRENCE

ST. LAWRENCE RIVER

THE FRENCH AND BRITISH SETTLED THE AREA IN THE 17th CENTURY.

CANADA IS THE WORLD'S SECOND-LARGEST COUNTRY IN AREA, BUT HAS ONLY 31,300,000 PEOPLE.

THE PAPER BUSINESS BEGAN IN 1803 IN A SMALL PAPER MILL HERE.

THIS IS THE OLDEST CITY IN CANADA.

QUEBEC

MANY TOURISTS VISIT HERE.

MONTREAL IS THE SECOND-LARGEST FRENCH-SPEAKING CITY IN THE WORLD.

PAPER PRODUCER

IRON ORE

MUCH OF QUEBEC STILL RETAINS STRONG FRENCH INFLUENCE.

THIS IS THE LARGEST PROVINCE.

A BLACK BEAR!

THE FIRST PERMANENT SETTLEMENT HERE WAS FOUNDED IN THE CITY OF QUEBEC BY SAMUEL CHAMPLAIN IN 1608.

OTTAWA IS THE CAPITAL OF CANADA.

CN TOWER

TORONTO

LAKE ONTARIO

QUEBEC

JAMES BAY

GEORGIAN BAY

LAKE HURON

LAKE ERIE

LAKE MICHIGAN

ONTARIO

THAT LOOKS LIKE FUN!

THERE WERE SOMETIMES AS MANY AS 2,000 PLAYERS ON THE FIELD!

ICE HOCKEY WAS INVENTED IN CANADA IN THE MID 1800s.

ONTARIO'S INDIANS USED TO PLAY A GAME CALLED BAGGATA, A FORERUNNER OF MODERN LACROSSE.

FOREST PRODUCTS

COPPER

LAKE SUPERIOR

UNITED STATES

NORTH

EAST

SOUTH

WEST

Canada is divided into ten provinces and three territories. Some of the eastern provinces were the first colonies to unite and form the Dominion of Canada. They had been the first areas in what is now Canada to be explored by Europeans.

LEARN ABOUT THIS AREA
AS YOU LOOK FOR THESE FUN ITEMS:

- ☐ Bear
- ☐ Beaver
- ☐ Beluga whale
- ☐ Boats (2)
- ☐ Caribou
- ☐ Goose
- ☐ Hockey puck
- ☐ Moose
- ☐ Porpoise
- ☐ Snowman
- ☐ Viking

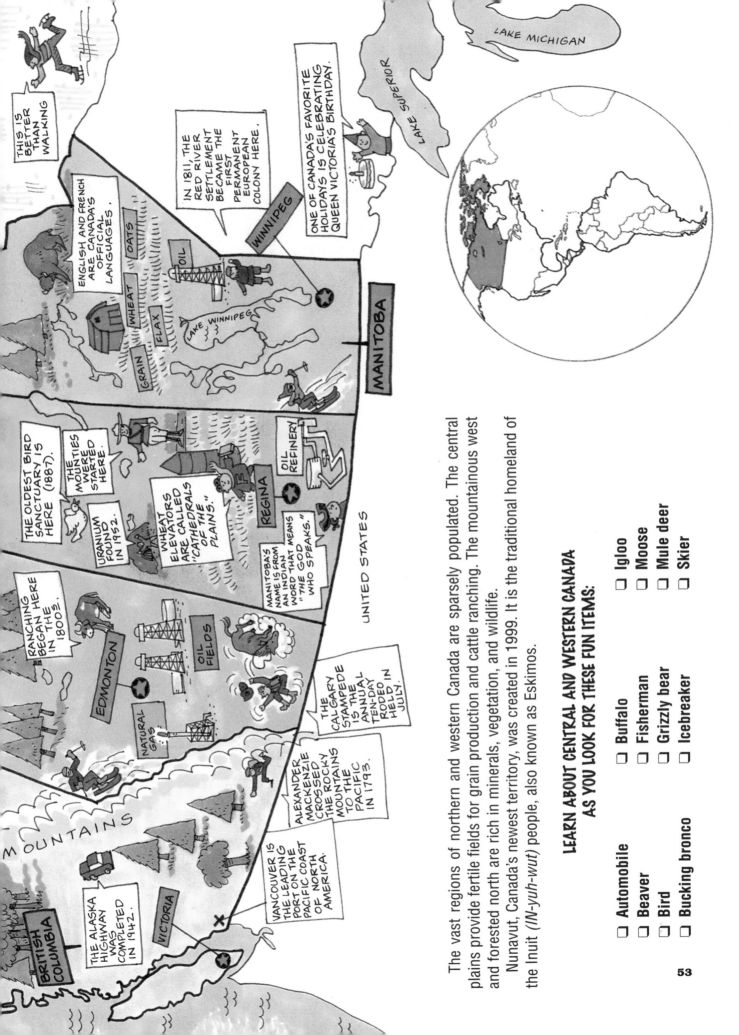

The vast regions of northern and western Canada are sparsely populated. The central plains provide fertile fields for grain production and cattle ranching. The mountainous west and forested north are rich in minerals, vegetation, and wildlife.

Nunavut, Canada's newest territory, was created in 1999. It is the traditional homeland of the Inuit (IN-yuh-wut) people, also known as Eskimos.

LEARN ABOUT CENTRAL AND WESTERN CANADA AS YOU LOOK FOR THESE FUN ITEMS:

- ☐ Automobile
- ☐ Beaver
- ☐ Bird
- ☐ Bucking bronco
- ☐ Buffalo
- ☐ Fisherman
- ☐ Grizzly bear
- ☐ Icebreaker
- ☐ Igloo
- ☐ Moose
- ☐ Mule deer
- ☐ Skier

53

THE UNITED STATES OF AMERICA

The United States of America is the world's third-largest country in population (after China and India) and the fourth-largest in land area (after Russia, China, and Canada). Its huge economic, political, and military influence make it the world's leading superpower.

In the 18th century, Britain ruled 13 American colonies. The U.S. became an independent nation in 1776, when it rebelled against British rule. Those colonies became the original 13 states. Today, the U.S. is a nation of 50 states. Washington, D.C., is the national capital and federal district. Outlying territories and other areas include Puerto Rico, the U.S. Virgin Islands, and Guam.

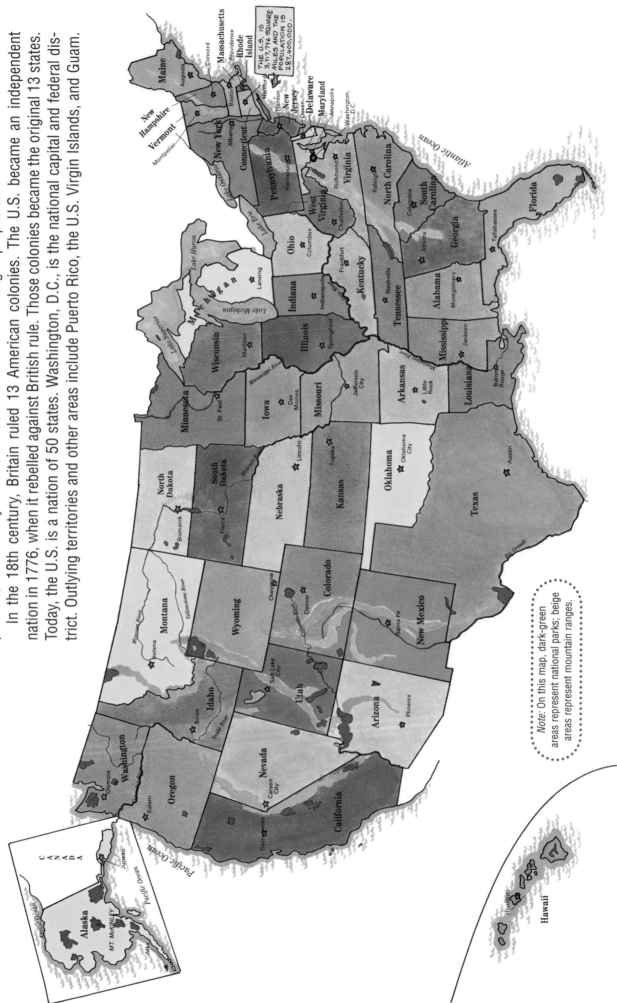

THE U.S. IS 3,717,796 SQUARE MILES AND THE POPULATION IS 287,400,000.

Note: On this map, dark-green areas represent national parks; beige areas represent mountain ranges.

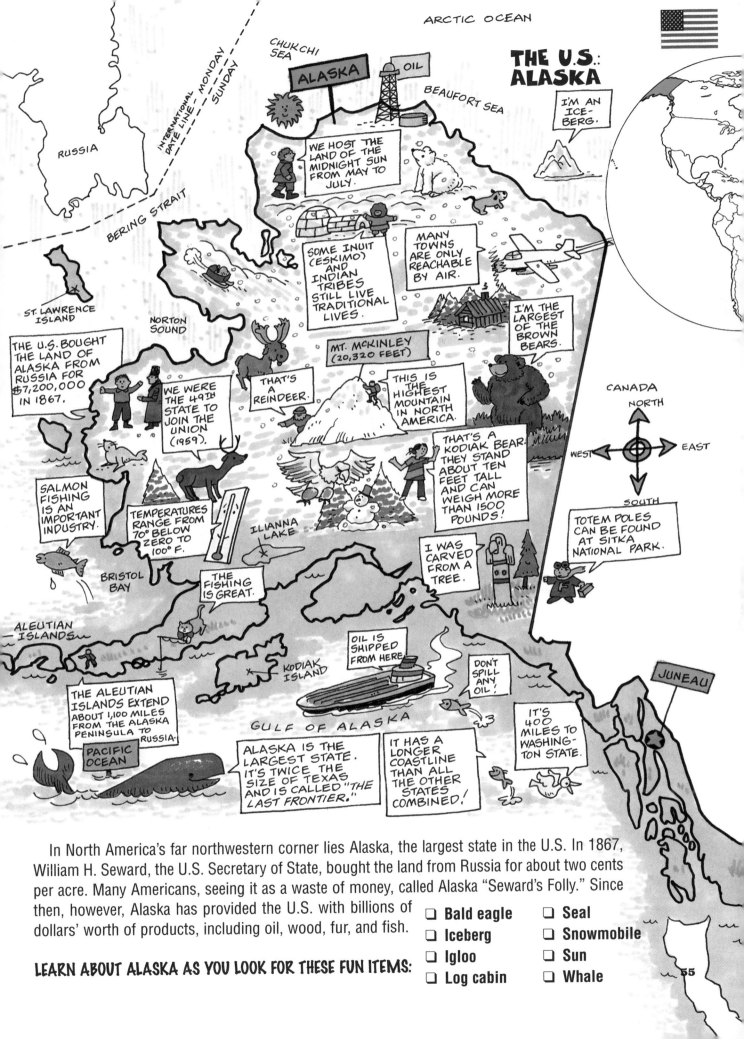

In North America's far northwestern corner lies Alaska, the largest state in the U.S. In 1867, William H. Seward, the U.S. Secretary of State, bought the land from Russia for about two cents per acre. Many Americans, seeing it as a waste of money, called Alaska "Seward's Folly." Since then, however, Alaska has provided the U.S. with billions of dollars' worth of products, including oil, wood, fur, and fish.

LEARN ABOUT ALASKA AS YOU LOOK FOR THESE FUN ITEMS:

- ☐ **Bald eagle**
- ☐ **Iceberg**
- ☐ **Igloo**
- ☐ **Log cabin**
- ☐ **Seal**
- ☐ **Snowmobile**
- ☐ **Sun**
- ☐ **Whale**

THE U.S.: THE WESTERN STATES

The western part of the country is characterized by deserts, mountains, river canyons, and great forests. Separated from the rest of the continental U.S. by the Rocky Mountains, parts of this area—especially along the coast—were rapidly settled and developed after railroads were built in the mid-19th century, linking west to east.

The Hawaiian Islands became a U.S. territory in 1900 and the 50th state in 1959.

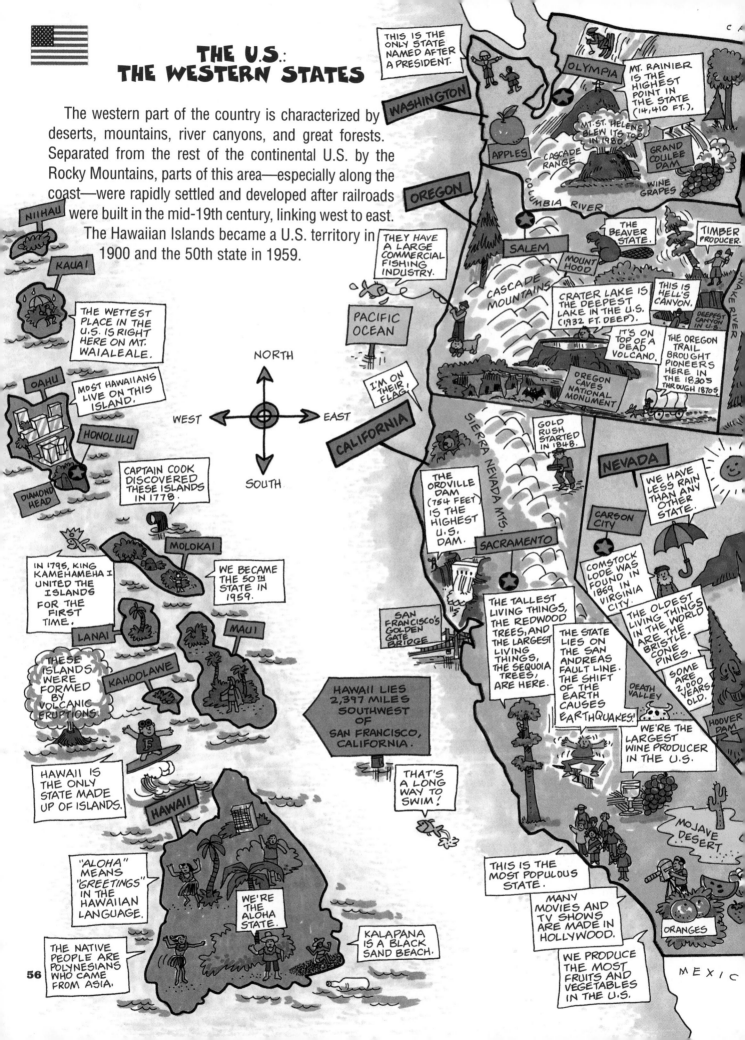

NORTH
WEST — EAST
SOUTH

THIS IS THE ONLY STATE NAMED AFTER A PRESIDENT.

WASHINGTON

OLYMPIA

MT. RAINIER IS THE HIGHEST POINT IN THE STATE (14,410 FT.).

MT. ST. HELENS BLEW ITS TOP IN 1980.

CASCADE RANGE

GRAND COULEE DAM

APPLES

WINE GRAPES

OREGON

COLUMBIA RIVER

THE BEAVER STATE.

TIMBER PRODUCER.

SALEM

MOUNT HOOD

CASCADE MOUNTAINS

CRATER LAKE IS THE DEEPEST LAKE IN THE U.S. (1,932 FT. DEEP).

THIS IS HELL'S CANYON.

DEEPEST CANYON IN U.S.

IT'S ON TOP OF A DEAD VOLCANO.

THE OREGON TRAIL BROUGHT PIONEERS HERE IN THE 1830S THROUGH 1870S.

OREGON CAVES NATIONAL MONUMENT

SNAKE RIVER

THEY HAVE A LARGE COMMERCIAL FISHING INDUSTRY.

PACIFIC OCEAN

I'M ON THEIR FLAG!

CALIFORNIA

SIERRA NEVADA MTS.

GOLD RUSH STARTED IN 1848.

NEVADA

WE HAVE LESS RAIN THAN ANY OTHER STATE.

CARSON CITY

THE OROVILLE DAM (754 FEET) IS THE HIGHEST U.S. DAM.

COMSTOCK LODE WAS FOUND IN 1869 IN VIRGINIA CITY.

SACRAMENTO

THE OLDEST LIVING THINGS IN THE WORLD ARE THE BRISTLE-CONE PINES.

SAN FRANCISCO'S GOLDEN GATE BRIDGE

THE TALLEST LIVING THINGS, THE REDWOOD TREES, AND THE LARGEST LIVING THINGS, THE SEQUOIA TREES, ARE HERE.

THE STATE LIES ON THE SAN ANDREAS FAULT LINE. THE SHIFT OF THE EARTH CAUSES EARTHQUAKES!

DEATH VALLEY

SOME ARE 2,000 YEARS OLD.

HOOVER DAM

WE'RE THE LARGEST WINE PRODUCER IN THE U.S.

MOJAVE DESERT

HAWAII LIES 2,397 MILES SOUTHWEST OF SAN FRANCISCO, CALIFORNIA.

THAT'S A LONG WAY TO SWIM!

THIS IS THE MOST POPULOUS STATE.

MANY MOVIES AND TV SHOWS ARE MADE IN HOLLYWOOD.

ORANGES

WE PRODUCE THE MOST FRUITS AND VEGETABLES IN THE U.S.

MEXICO

Hawaiian Islands

NIIHAU

KAUAI

THE WETTEST PLACE IN THE U.S. IS RIGHT HERE ON MT. WAIALEALE.

OAHU

MOST HAWAIIANS LIVE ON THIS ISLAND.

HONOLULU

DIAMOND HEAD

CAPTAIN COOK DISCOVERED THESE ISLANDS IN 1778.

MOLOKAI

IN 1795, KING KAMEHAMEHA I UNITED THE ISLANDS FOR THE FIRST TIME.

WE BECAME THE 50TH STATE IN 1959.

LANAI

MAUI

THESE ISLANDS WERE FORMED BY VOLCANIC ERUPTIONS.

KAHOOLAWE

HAWAII IS THE ONLY STATE MADE UP OF ISLANDS.

HAWAII

"ALOHA" MEANS "GREETINGS" IN THE HAWAIIAN LANGUAGE.

WE'RE THE ALOHA STATE.

KALAPANA IS A BLACK SAND BEACH.

THE NATIVE PEOPLE ARE POLYNESIANS WHO CAME FROM ASIA.

LEARN ABOUT THE U.S.A.'S WESTERN STATES AS YOU LOOK FOR THESE FUN ITEMS:

- ☐ Automobile
- ☐ Balloon
- ☐ Beaver
- ☐ Bee
- ☐ Bone
- ☐ Brush
- ☐ Camera
- ☐ Covered wagons (3)
- ☐ Flying bat
- ☐ Orange
- ☐ Paper airplane
- ☐ Periscope
- ☐ Skier
- ☐ Sun
- ☐ Surfer
- ☐ Umbrellas (2)

THE U.S.: THE MIDWESTERN STATES

Bordered by the Great Lakes to the north, the Rocky Mountains to the west, and the Appalachian Mountains to the east is a flat, fertile area known as the Great Plains. It produces more than half of the world's corn and enough wheat to make the U.S. the world's largest exporter.

LEARN ABOUT THE U.S.A.'S MIDWESTERN STATES AS YOU LOOK FOR THESE FUN ITEMS:

- ❑ Blue ox
- ❑ Book
- ❑ Cereal
- ❑ Flower
- ❑ Football
- ❑ Heart
- ❑ Race cars (3)
- ❑ Santa Claus
- ❑ Snowman
- ❑ Tire
- ❑ Watermelon slice
- ❑ Woolly mammoth

THE U.S.: THE NORTHEASTERN AND MIDATLANTIC STATES

The most populous region in the country, the northeast and midatlantic states were the first to be settled by Europeans. Colonists arrived from England in 1620 and settled in New Plymouth, Massachusetts.

LEARN ABOUT U.S.A.'S NORTHEASTERN AND MIDATLANTIC STATES AS YOU LOOK FOR THESE FUN ITEMS:

- ❑ Anchor
- ❑ Apple
- ❑ Baseball
- ❑ Basketball
- ❑ Cannon
- ❑ Kite
- ❑ Lighthouse
- ❑ Lobster
- ❑ Ship
- ❑ Skier
- ❑ Treasure chest
- ❑ Truck
- ❑ Umbrella

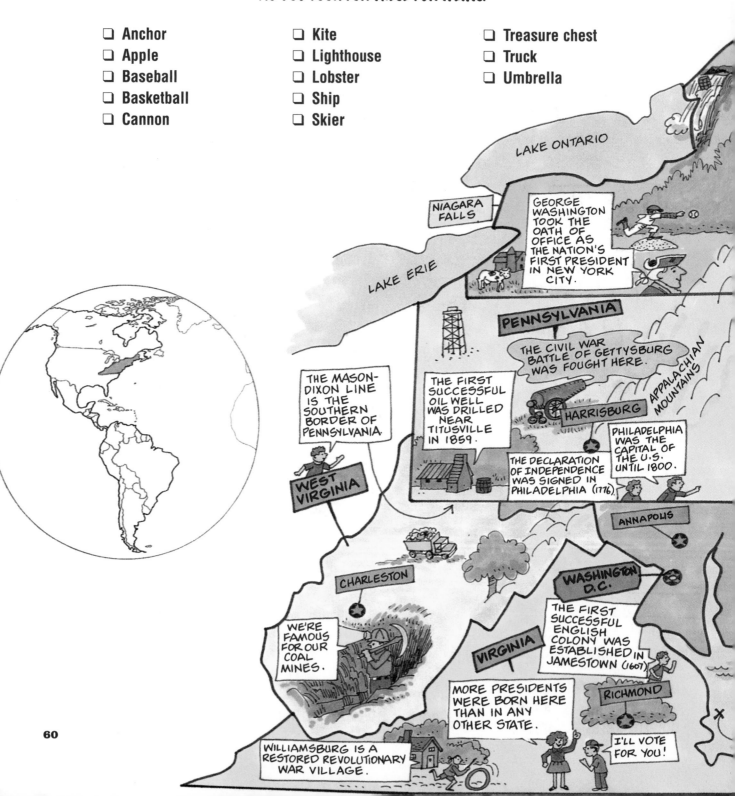

LAKE ONTARIO

NIAGARA FALLS

GEORGE WASHINGTON TOOK THE OATH OF OFFICE AS THE NATION'S FIRST PRESIDENT IN NEW YORK CITY.

LAKE ERIE

PENNSYLVANIA

THE CIVIL WAR BATTLE OF GETTYSBURG WAS FOUGHT HERE.

APPALACHIAN MOUNTAINS

THE MASON-DIXON LINE IS THE SOUTHERN BORDER OF PENNSYLVANIA.

THE FIRST SUCCESSFUL OIL WELL WAS DRILLED NEAR TITUSVILLE IN 1859.

HARRISBURG

PHILADELPHIA WAS THE CAPITAL OF THE U.S. UNTIL 1800.

THE DECLARATION OF INDEPENDENCE WAS SIGNED IN PHILADELPHIA (1776).

WEST VIRGINIA

ANNAPOLIS

CHARLESTON

WASHINGTON D.C.

WE'RE FAMOUS FOR OUR COAL MINES.

VIRGINIA

THE FIRST SUCCESSFUL ENGLISH COLONY WAS ESTABLISHED IN JAMESTOWN (1607)

MORE PRESIDENTS WERE BORN HERE THAN IN ANY OTHER STATE.

RICHMOND

I'LL VOTE FOR YOU!

WILLIAMSBURG IS A RESTORED REVOLUTIONARY WAR VILLAGE.

The southern states, which extend from the Atlantic coast to Texas, were once totally farm based, producing mainly cotton and tobacco. Although still agricultural, the area is now strong in industry, and produces oil as well as iron and steel.

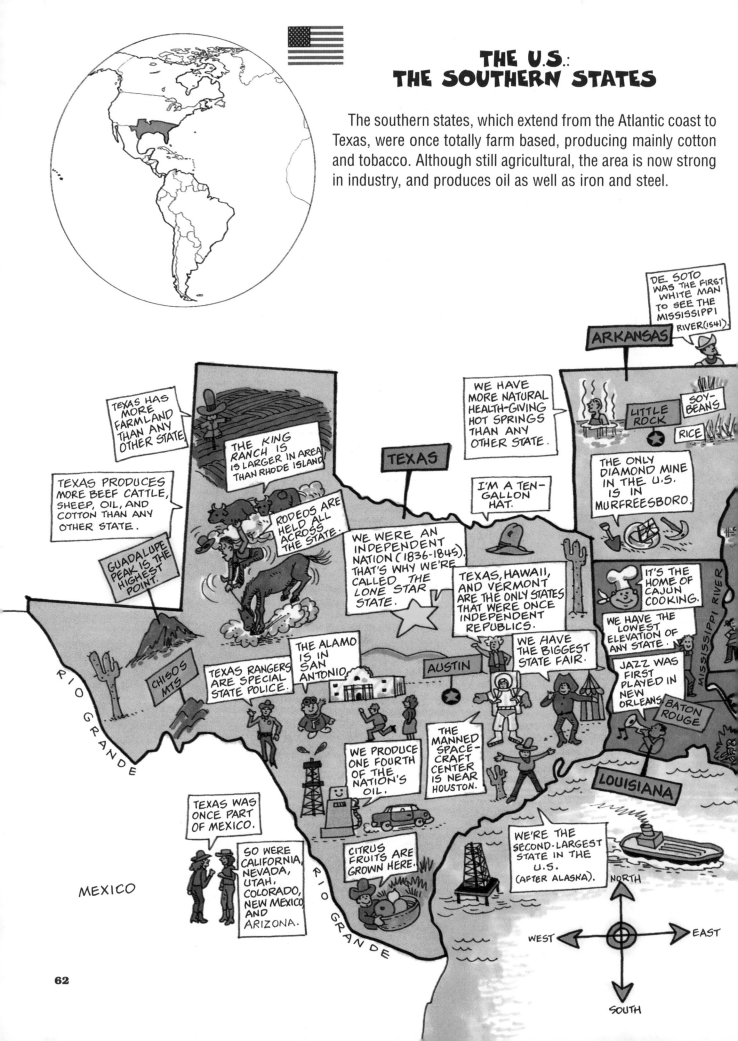

DE SOTO WAS THE FIRST WHITE MAN TO SEE THE MISSISSIPPI RIVER (1541).

ARKANSAS

WE HAVE MORE NATURAL HEALTH-GIVING HOT SPRINGS THAN ANY OTHER STATE.

LITTLE ROCK

SOY-BEANS

RICE

THE ONLY DIAMOND MINE IN THE U.S. IS IN MURFREESBORO.

TEXAS HAS MORE FARMLAND THAN ANY OTHER STATE.

THE KING RANCH IS LARGER IN AREA THAN RHODE ISLAND.

TEXAS

I'M A TEN-GALLON HAT.

TEXAS PRODUCES MORE BEEF CATTLE, SHEEP, OIL, AND COTTON THAN ANY OTHER STATE.

RODEOS ARE HELD ALL ACROSS THE STATE.

WE WERE AN INDEPENDENT NATION (1836-1845). THAT'S WHY WE'RE CALLED THE LONE STAR STATE.

TEXAS, HAWAII, AND VERMONT ARE THE ONLY STATES THAT WERE ONCE INDEPENDENT REPUBLICS.

IT'S THE HOME OF CAJUN COOKING.

GUADALUPE PEAK IS THE HIGHEST POINT.

WE HAVE THE LOWEST ELEVATION OF ANY STATE.

MISSISSIPPI RIVER

RIO GRANDE

CHISOS MTS

TEXAS RANGERS ARE SPECIAL STATE POLICE.

THE ALAMO IS IN SAN ANTONIO.

AUSTIN

WE HAVE THE BIGGEST STATE FAIR.

JAZZ WAS FIRST PLAYED IN NEW ORLEANS.

BATON ROUGE

THE MANNED SPACE-CRAFT CENTER IS NEAR HOUSTON.

WE PRODUCE ONE FOURTH OF THE NATION'S OIL.

LOUISIANA

TEXAS WAS ONCE PART OF MEXICO.

SO WERE CALIFORNIA, NEVADA, UTAH, COLORADO, NEW MEXICO, AND ARIZONA.

CITRUS FRUITS ARE GROWN HERE.

WE'RE THE SECOND-LARGEST STATE IN THE U.S. (AFTER ALASKA).

MEXICO

RIO GRANDE

NORTH
WEST
EAST
SOUTH

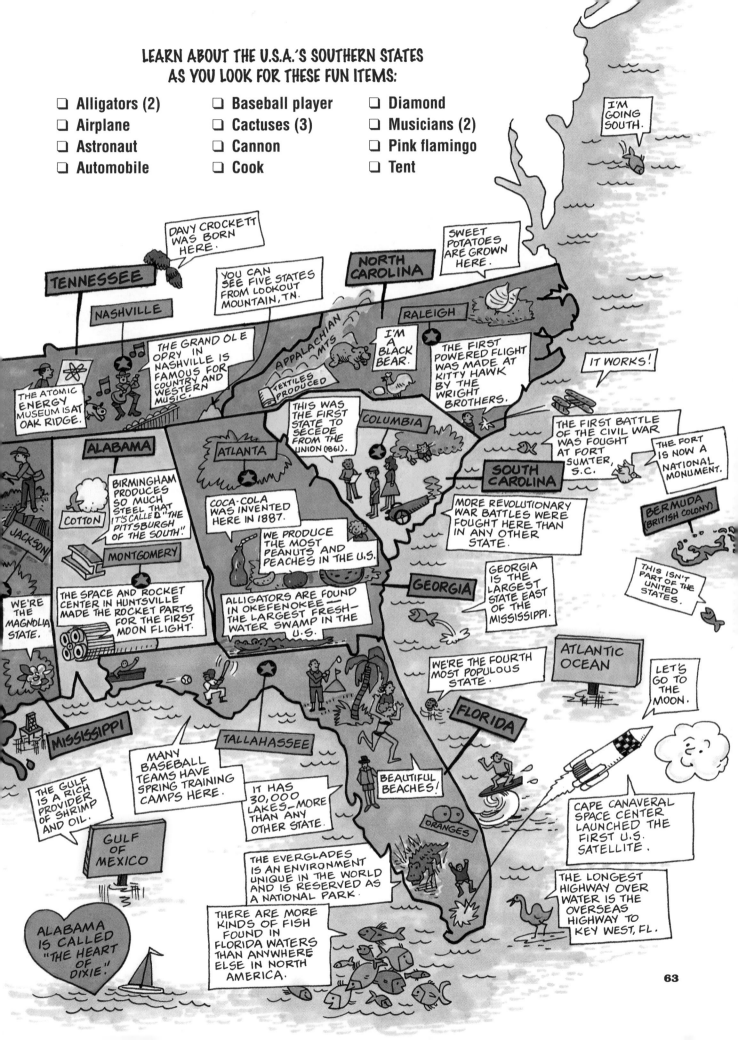

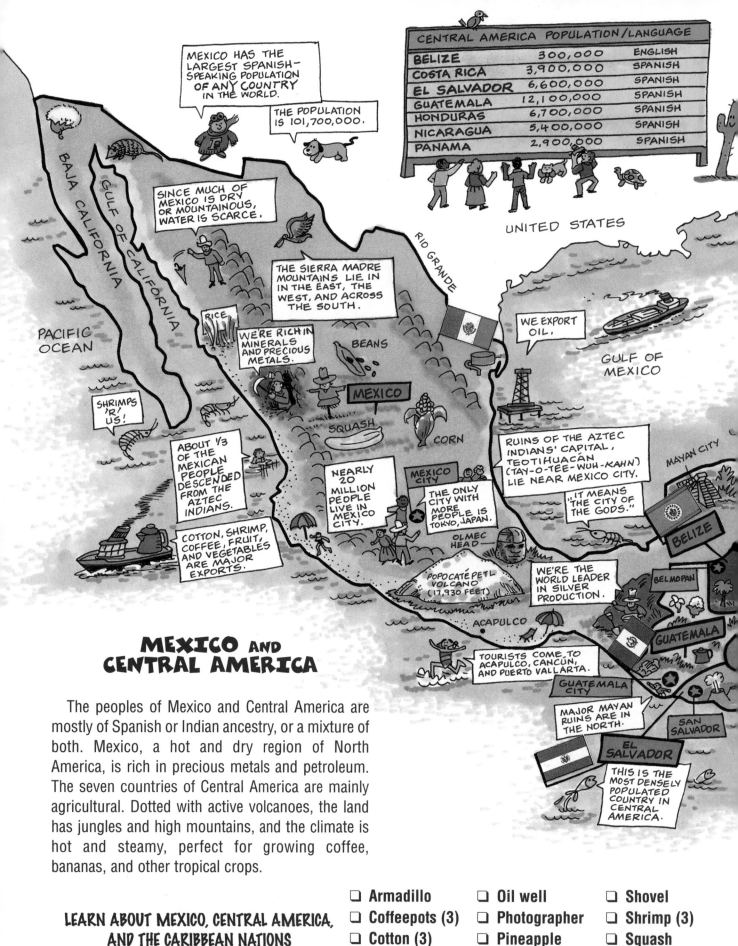

CENTRAL AMERICA POPULATION/LANGUAGE		
BELIZE	300,000	ENGLISH
COSTA RICA	3,900,000	SPANISH
EL SALVADOR	6,600,000	SPANISH
GUATEMALA	12,100,000	SPANISH
HONDURAS	6,700,000	SPANISH
NICARAGUA	5,400,000	SPANISH
PANAMA	2,900,000	SPANISH

MEXICO AND CENTRAL AMERICA

The peoples of Mexico and Central America are mostly of Spanish or Indian ancestry, or a mixture of both. Mexico, a hot and dry region of North America, is rich in precious metals and petroleum. The seven countries of Central America are mainly agricultural. Dotted with active volcanoes, the land has jungles and high mountains, and the climate is hot and steamy, perfect for growing coffee, bananas, and other tropical crops.

LEARN ABOUT MEXICO, CENTRAL AMERICA, AND THE CARIBBEAN NATIONS AS YOU LOOK FOR THESE FUN ITEMS:

- ❑ Armadillo
- ❑ Coffeepots (3)
- ❑ Cotton (3)
- ❑ Diver
- ❑ Miner
- ❑ Oil well
- ❑ Photographer
- ❑ Pineapple
- ❑ Sailor
- ❑ Scarecrow
- ❑ Shovel
- ❑ Shrimp (3)
- ❑ Squash
- ❑ Turtle
- ❑ Umbrellas (3)

THE CARIBBEAN NATIONS

A chain of tropical islands about 2,000 miles long stretches across the Caribbean Sea, then curves like a hook toward South America. These islands were the first land in the Americas that Christopher Columbus saw and set foot on during his 1492 voyage of discovery. In the 16th century, Europeans colonized the islands, bringing African slaves to work plantations.

Today, 13 of the islands or island groups are independent nations (see list below). Others are territories of the U.S. or European countries. Most of the people living here are descendants of African slaves, Spanish conquerors, or both. Most countries in this region depend on tourism and agriculture for their income.

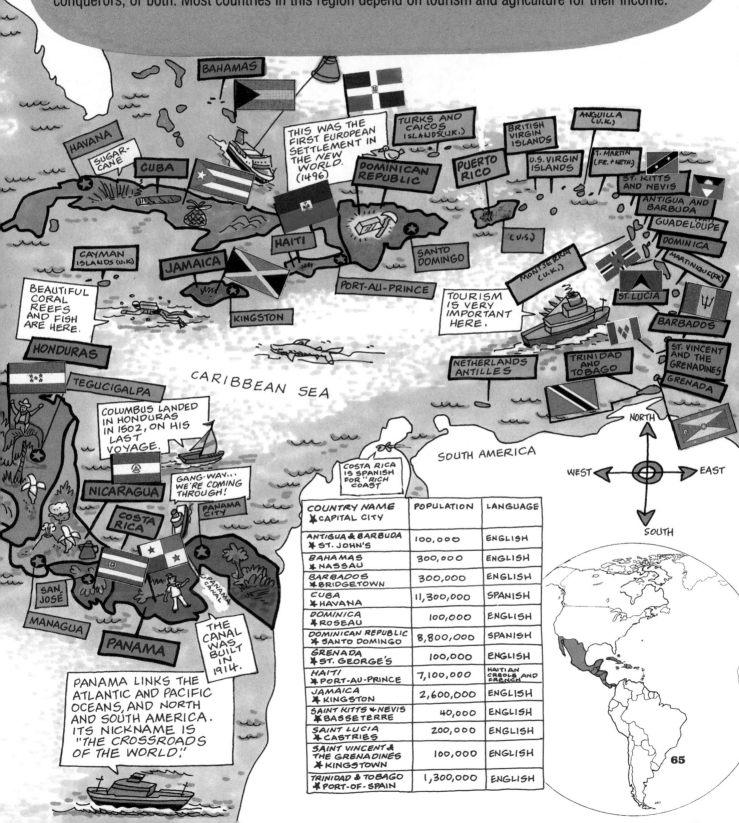

BAHAMAS

HAVANA

SUGAR-CANE

CUBA

THIS WAS THE FIRST EUROPEAN SETTLEMENT IN THE NEW WORLD. (1496)

TURKS AND CAICOS ISLANDS (U.K.)

DOMINICAN REPUBLIC

PUERTO RICO

BRITISH VIRGIN ISLANDS

ANGUILLA (U.K.)

U.S. VIRGIN ISLANDS

ST. MARTIN (FR. + NETH.)

ST. KITTS AND NEVIS

ANTIGUA AND BARBUDA

GUADELOUPE

DOMINICA

MARTINIQUE (FR.)

HAITI

CAYMAN ISLANDS (U.K.)

JAMAICA

SANTO DOMINGO

(U.S.)

MONTSERRAT (U.K.)

ST. LUCIA

BARBADOS

BEAUTIFUL CORAL REEFS AND FISH ARE HERE.

PORT-AU-PRINCE

TOURISM IS VERY IMPORTANT HERE.

ST. VINCENT AND THE GRENADINES

GRENADA

KINGSTON

HONDURAS

TEGUCIGALPA

CARIBBEAN SEA

NETHERLANDS ANTILLES

TRINIDAD AND TOBAGO

COLUMBUS LANDED IN HONDURAS IN 1502, ON HIS LAST VOYAGE.

SOUTH AMERICA

NORTH

GANG-WAY... WE'RE COMING THROUGH!

NICARAGUA

COSTA RICA

PANAMA CITY

COSTA RICA IS SPANISH FOR "RICH COAST"

WEST

EAST

SOUTH

SAN JOSE

MANAGUA

PANAMA

PANAMA CANAL

THE CANAL WAS BUILT IN 1914.

PANAMA LINKS THE ATLANTIC AND PACIFIC OCEANS, AND NORTH AND SOUTH AMERICA. ITS NICKNAME IS "THE CROSSROADS OF THE WORLD."

COUNTRY NAME ✱ CAPITAL CITY	POPULATION	LANGUAGE
ANTIGUA & BARBUDA ✱ ST. JOHN'S	100,000	ENGLISH
BAHAMAS ✱ NASSAU	300,000	ENGLISH
BARBADOS ✱ BRIDGETOWN	300,000	ENGLISH
CUBA ✱ HAVANA	11,300,000	SPANISH
DOMINICA ✱ ROSEAU	100,000	ENGLISH
DOMINICAN REPUBLIC ✱ SANTO DOMINGO	8,800,000	SPANISH
GRENADA ✱ ST. GEORGE'S	100,000	ENGLISH
HAITI ✱ PORT-AU-PRINCE	7,100,000	HAITIAN CREOLE AND FRENCH
JAMAICA ✱ KINGSTON	2,600,000	ENGLISH
SAINT KITTS & NEVIS ✱ BASSETERRE	40,000	ENGLISH
SAINT LUCIA ✱ CASTRIES	200,000	ENGLISH
SAINT VINCENT & THE GRENADINES ✱ KINGSTOWN	100,000	ENGLISH
TRINIDAD & TOBAGO ✱ PORT-OF-SPAIN	1,300,000	ENGLISH

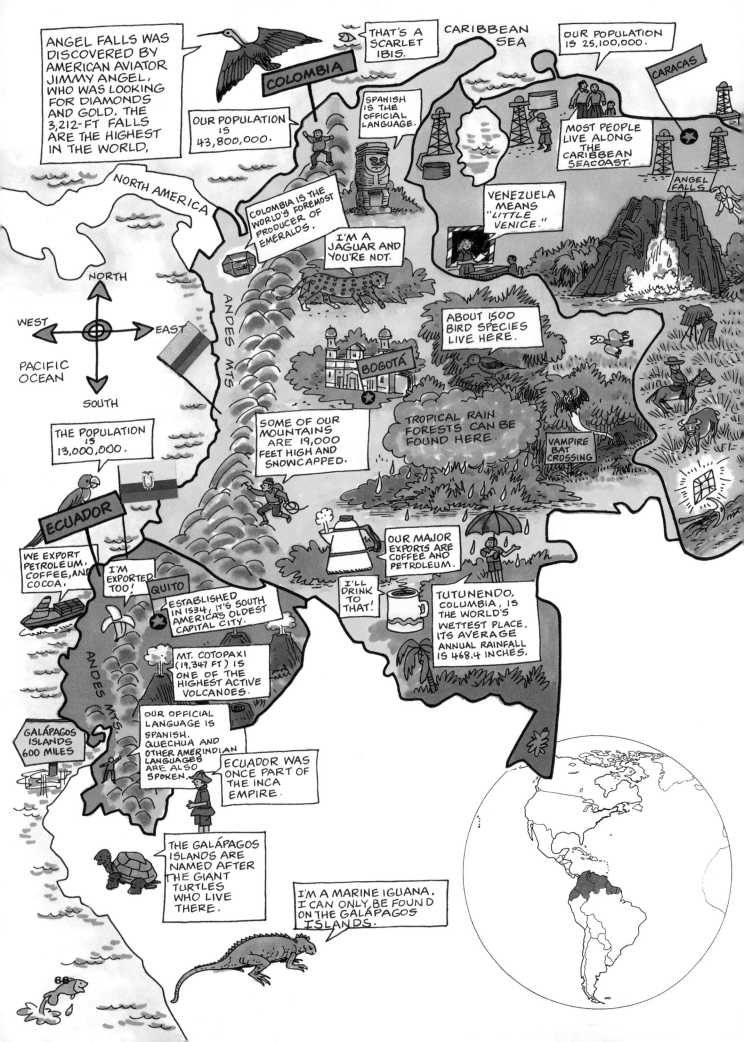

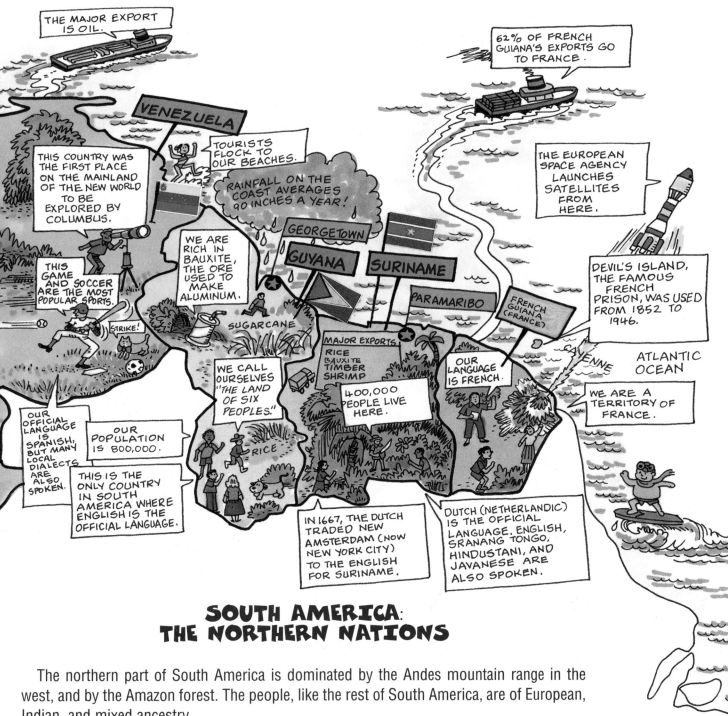

SOUTH AMERICA: THE NORTHERN NATIONS

The northern part of South America is dominated by the Andes mountain range in the west, and by the Amazon forest. The people, like the rest of South America, are of European, Indian, and mixed ancestry.

Once Spanish colonies, Ecuador, Colombia, and Venezuela won their independence in the early decades of the 19th century. Guyana and Suriname gained their independence only recently: Guyana in 1966, from Britain; and Suriname in 1975, from the Netherlands. French Guiana is the only country on the South American mainland that is still a European territory.

LEARN ABOUT SOUTH AMERICA'S NORTHERN NATIONS AS YOU LOOK FOR THESE FUN ITEMS:

- ❏ Aluminum can
- ❏ Angel
- ❏ Baseball bat
- ❏ Bat
- ❏ Cup
- ❏ Emerald
- ❏ Ibis
- ❏ Iguana
- ❏ Jaguar
- ❏ Mountain climber
- ❏ Photographer
- ❏ Satellite rocket
- ❏ Schoolteacher
- ❏ Soccer ball
- ❏ Stone idol
- ❏ Surfer
- ❏ Telescope
- ❏ Turtle

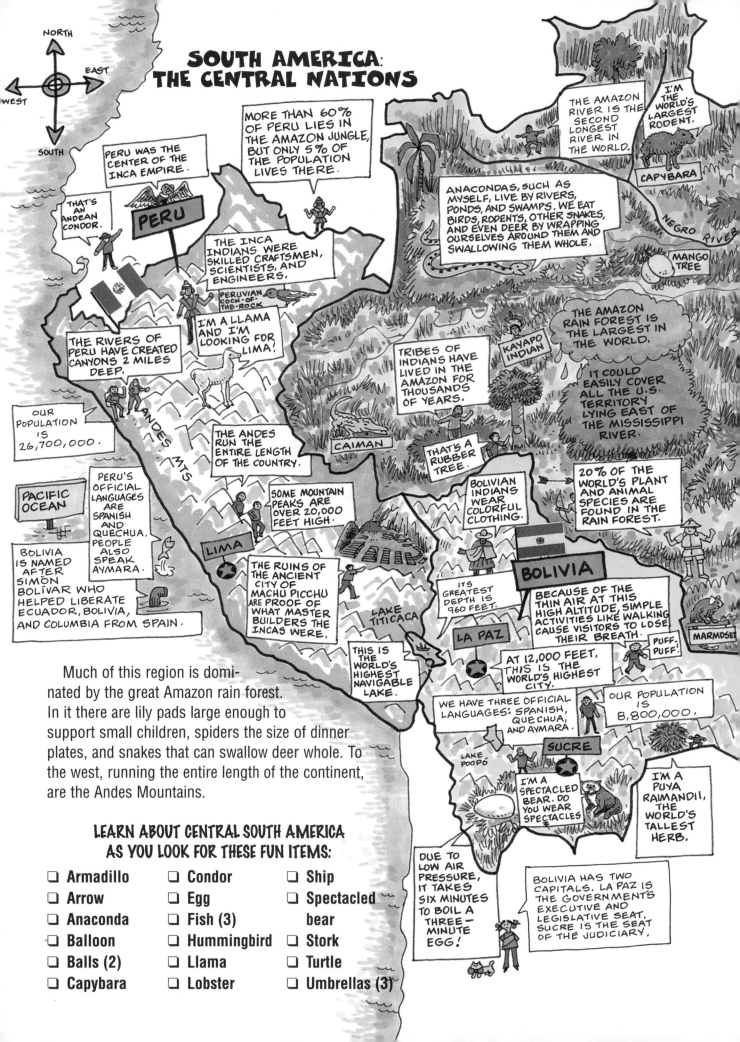

SOUTH AMERICA: THE CENTRAL NATIONS

NORTH **EAST** **WEST** **SOUTH**

PERU WAS THE CENTER OF THE INCA EMPIRE.

MORE THAN 60% OF PERU LIES IN THE AMAZON JUNGLE, BUT ONLY 5% OF THE POPULATION LIVES THERE.

THE AMAZON RIVER IS THE SECOND LONGEST RIVER IN THE WORLD.

I'M THE WORLD'S LARGEST RODENT.

THAT'S AN ANDEAN CONDOR.

PERU

ANACONDAS, SUCH AS MYSELF, LIVE BY RIVERS, PONDS, AND SWAMPS. WE EAT BIRDS, RODENTS, OTHER SNAKES, AND EVEN DEER BY WRAPPING OURSELVES AROUND THEM AND SWALLOWING THEM WHOLE.

CAPYBARA

THE INCA INDIANS WERE SKILLED CRAFTSMEN, SCIENTISTS, AND ENGINEERS.

PERUVIAN COCK-OF-THE-ROCK

NEGRO RIVER

MANGO TREE

THE RIVERS OF PERU HAVE CREATED CANYONS 2 MILES DEEP.

I'M A LLAMA AND I'M LOOKING FOR LIMA!

THE AMAZON RAIN FOREST IS THE LARGEST IN THE WORLD.

KAYAPO INDIAN

TRIBES OF INDIANS HAVE LIVED IN THE AMAZON FOR THOUSANDS OF YEARS.

IT COULD EASILY COVER ALL THE U.S. TERRITORY LYING EAST OF THE MISSISSIPPI RIVER.

OUR POPULATION IS 26,700,000.

THE ANDES RUN THE ENTIRE LENGTH OF THE COUNTRY.

CAIMAN

THAT'S A RUBBER TREE.

ANDES MTS

PACIFIC OCEAN

PERU'S OFFICIAL LANGUAGES ARE SPANISH AND QUECHUA. PEOPLE ALSO SPEAK AYMARA.

SOME MOUNTAIN PEAKS ARE OVER 20,000 FEET HIGH.

BOLIVIAN INDIANS WEAR COLORFUL CLOTHING.

20% OF THE WORLD'S PLANT AND ANIMAL SPECIES ARE FOUND IN THE RAIN FOREST.

BOLIVIA IS NAMED AFTER SIMON BOLIVAR WHO HELPED LIBERATE ECUADOR, BOLIVIA, AND COLUMBIA FROM SPAIN.

LIMA

THE RUINS OF THE ANCIENT CITY OF MACHU PICCHU ARE PROOF OF WHAT MASTER BUILDERS THE INCAS WERE.

BOLIVIA

MARMOSET

ITS GREATEST DEPTH IS 960 FEET.

BECAUSE OF THE THIN AIR AT THIS HIGH ALTITUDE, SIMPLE ACTIVITIES LIKE WALKING CAUSE VISITORS TO LOSE THEIR BREATH.

PUFF. PUFF!

LAKE TITICACA

THIS IS THE WORLD'S HIGHEST NAVIGABLE LAKE.

LA PAZ

AT 12,000 FEET, THIS IS THE WORLD'S HIGHEST CITY.

Much of this region is dominated by the great Amazon rain forest. In it there are lily pads large enough to support small children, spiders the size of dinner plates, and snakes that can swallow deer whole. To the west, running the entire length of the continent, are the Andes Mountains.

WE HAVE THREE OFFICIAL LANGUAGES: SPANISH, QUECHUA, AND AYMARA.

OUR POPULATION IS 8,800,000.

LAKE POOPÓ

SUCRE

I'M A SPECTACLED BEAR. DO YOU WEAR SPECTACLES?

I'M A PUYA RAIMANDII, THE WORLD'S TALLEST HERB.

LEARN ABOUT CENTRAL SOUTH AMERICA AS YOU LOOK FOR THESE FUN ITEMS:

- ☐ Armadillo
- ☐ Arrow
- ☐ Anaconda
- ☐ Balloon
- ☐ Balls (2)
- ☐ Capybara
- ☐ Condor
- ☐ Egg
- ☐ Fish (3)
- ☐ Hummingbird
- ☐ Llama
- ☐ Lobster
- ☐ Ship
- ☐ Spectacled bear
- ☐ Stork
- ☐ Turtle
- ☐ Umbrellas (3)

DUE TO LOW AIR PRESSURE, IT TAKES SIX MINUTES TO BOIL A THREE-MINUTE EGG!

BOLIVIA HAS TWO CAPITALS. LA PAZ IS THE GOVERNMENT'S EXECUTIVE AND LEGISLATIVE SEAT. SUCRE IS THE SEAT OF THE JUDICIARY.

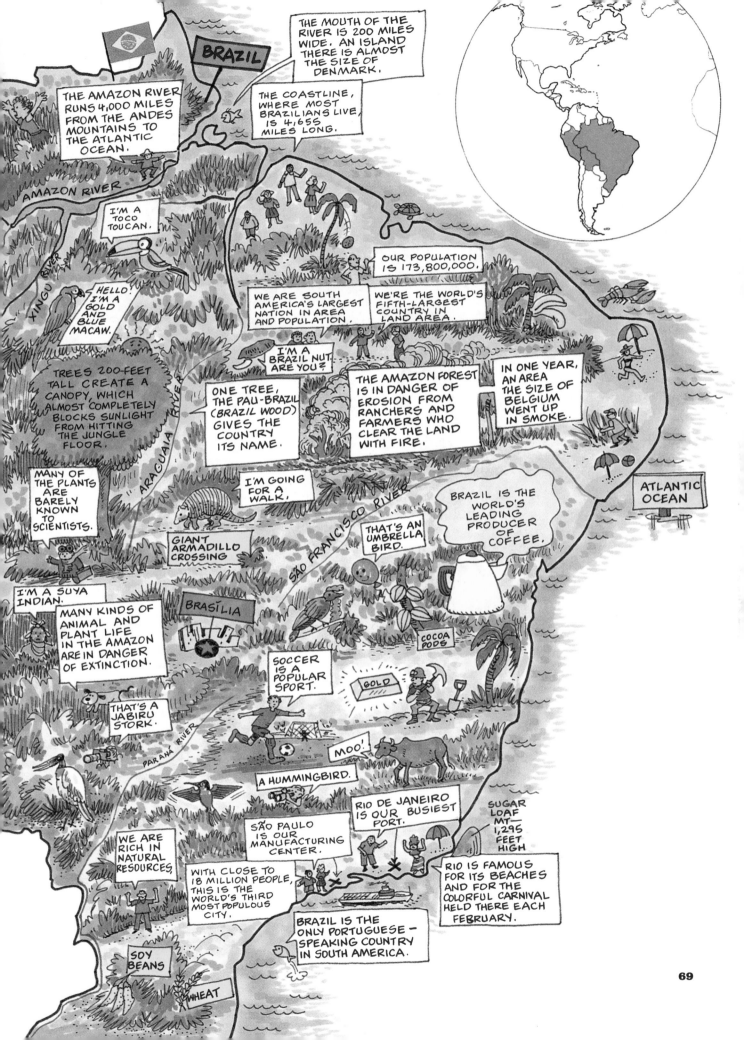

69

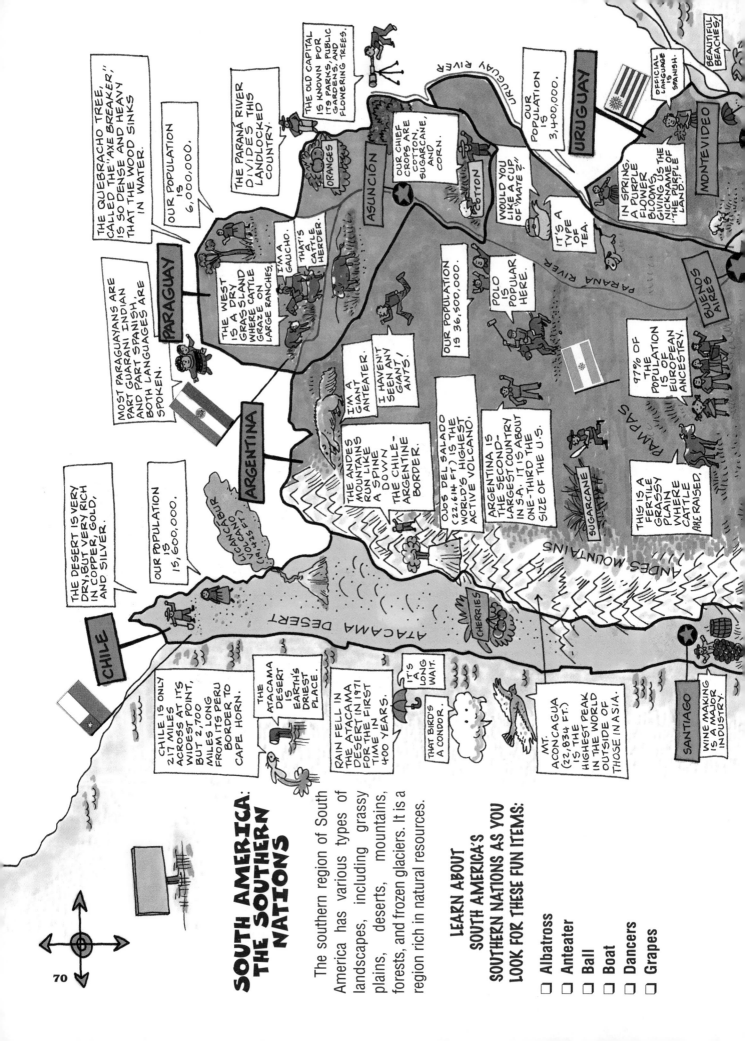

SOUTH AMERICA: THE SOUTHERN NATIONS

The southern region of South America has various types of landscapes, including grassy plains, deserts, mountains, forests, and frozen glaciers. It is a region rich in natural resources.

LEARN ABOUT SOUTH AMERICA'S SOUTHERN NATIONS AS YOU LOOK FOR THESE FUN ITEMS:

- ☐ Albatross
- ☐ Anteater
- ☐ Ball
- ☐ Boat
- ☐ Dancers
- ☐ Grapes

70

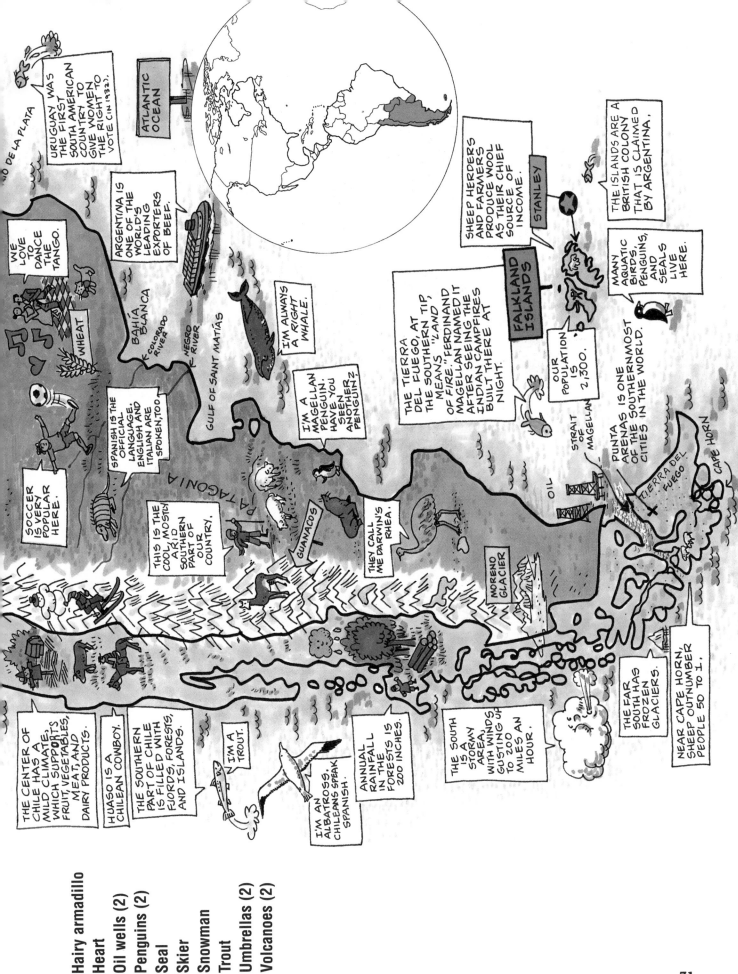

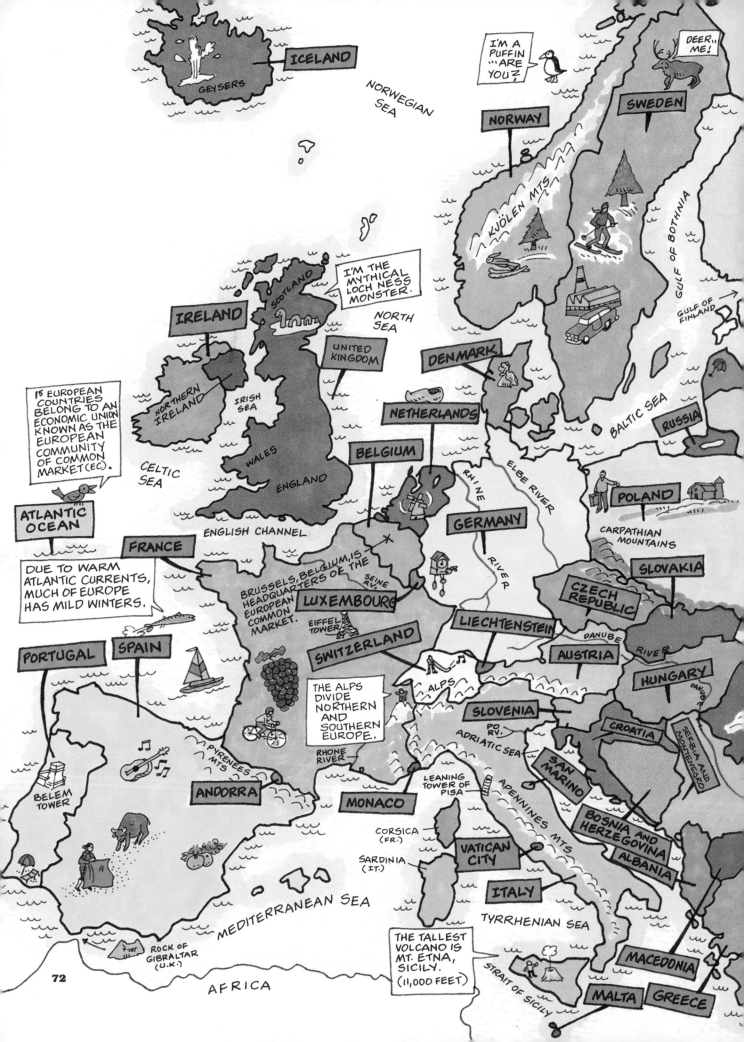

EUROPE

The seat of Western civilization, Europe has had a strong influence on the world through trade, exploration, and industry.

The continent stretches from the icy Arctic Circle in the north to the warm Mediterranean Sea in the south. Its western border is the North Atlantic Ocean and its eastern borders are the Ural and Caucasus mountains. The land—with its fertile plains and tall mountains—is as varied as its countries, peoples, and cultures.

LEARN ABOUT EUROPE AS YOU LOOK FOR THESE FUN ITEMS:

- ☐ Cyclist
- ☐ Eiffel Tower
- ☐ Fish (3)
- ☐ Grapes
- ☐ Puffin
- ☐ Sailboat
- ☐ Volcano
- ☐ Windmill
- ☐ Wooden shoe

FINLAND

RUSSIA

LAKE LADOGA

ESTONIA

LATVIA

LITHUANIA

BELARUS

FLAX

SUGAR BEETS

UKRAINE

MOLDOVA

WHEAT

DNIEPER RV.

DON RIVER

VOLGA RIVER

HIGHEST POINT IN EUROPE IS MT. ELBRUS IN THE CAUCASUS RANGE IN RUSSIA.

CAUCASUS MTS

THE VOLGA (RUNNING FOR 2,290 MILES) IS THE LONGEST RIVER IN EUROPE.

CASPIAN SEA

EUROPE IS CONSIDERED THE BIRTHPLACE OF WESTERN CIVILIZATION.

ROMANIA

TRANSYLVANIAN ALPS

THE DANUBE RIVER FLOWS THROUGH 7 EUROPEAN COUNTRIES.

THE BLACK SEA

NORTH

EAST

WEST

SOUTH

BULGARIA

TURKEY

AEGEAN SEA

EUROPE IS THE WORLD'S SECOND SMALLEST CONTINENT. (ONLY AUSTRALIA IS SMALLER.) YET IT RANKS THIRD IN POPULATION, AFTER ASIA AND AFRICA.

EUROPE HAS AN AREA OF ABOUT 4,000,000 SQUARE MILES.

ITS POPULATION IS 728,000,000.

THE LARGEST LAKE IN EUROPE IS LADOGA, RUSSIA (7,000 SQ. MILES).

UNITED KINGDOM AND IRELAND

The United Kingdom is a country made up of four parts: England, Wales, Scotland, and Northern Ireland. (The first three are also known as Britain.) Northern Ireland is on the same large island as the independent country of Ireland. In the late 19th and early 20th centuries, Great Britain was the world's leading industrial and trading nation. Its worldwide empire included Canada, India, Australia, New Zealand, and parts of Africa.

LEARN ABOUT THE UNITED KINGDOM AND IRELAND AS YOU LOOK FOR THESE FUN ITEMS:

- ☐ Bagpipe
- ☐ Big Ben
- ☐ Bus
- ☐ Deer
- ☐ Ferry
- ☐ Four-leaf clover
- ☐ Golf
- ☐ Knight in armor
- ☐ Lobster
- ☐ "Nessie"
- ☐ Sheep (3)
- ☐ Soccer ball
- ☐ Tennis racket

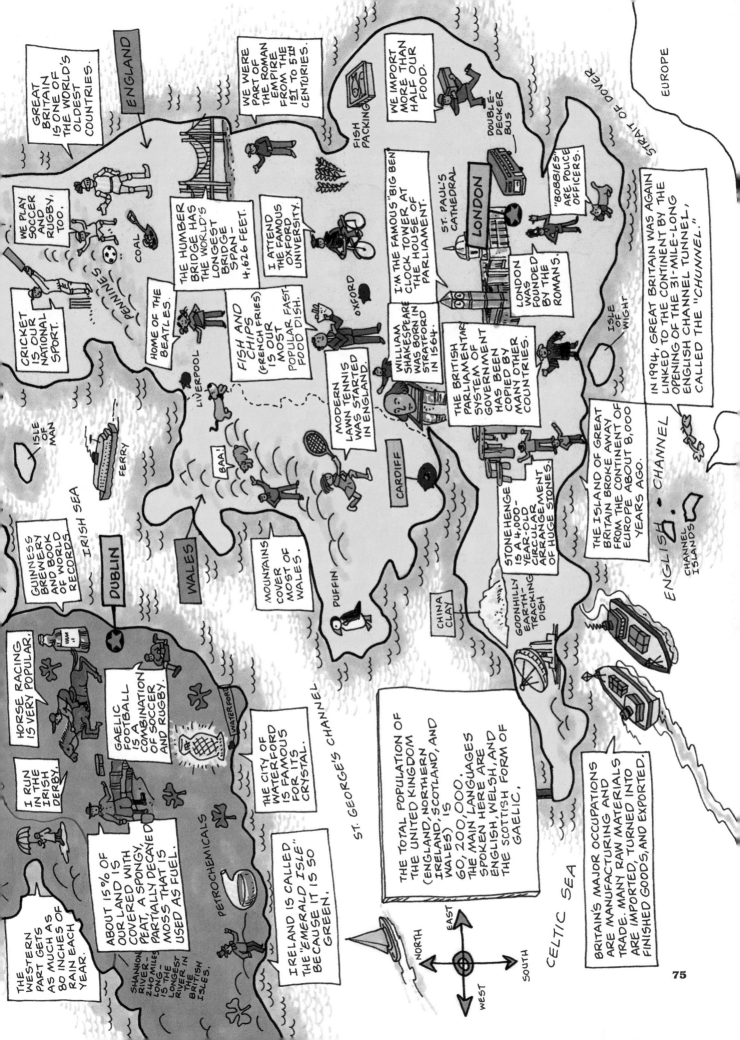

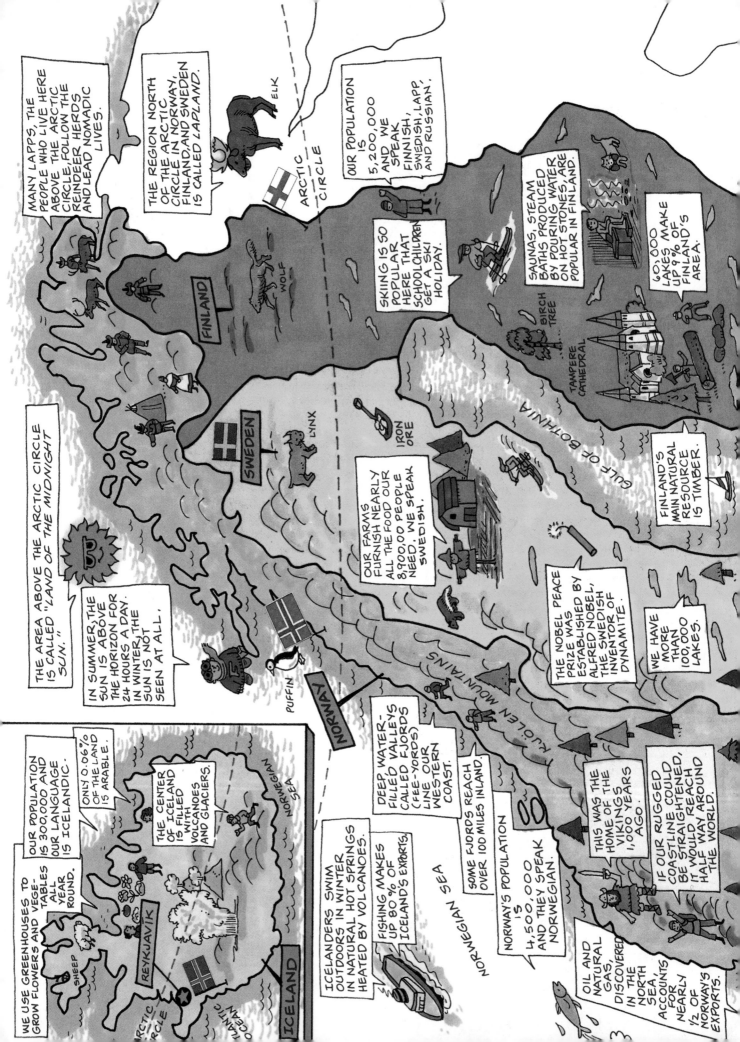

SCANDINAVIA

The peninsular countries of Norway, Sweden, and Denmark form the region known as Scandinavia. Most geographers also include Finland and Iceland in that region. Many Scandinavians are descendants of the seafaring Vikings, who lived in this region about a thousand years ago. The land is rich in natural resources, and Scandinavians enjoy one of the highest standards of living in the world.

LEARN ABOUT SCANDINAVIA
AS YOU LOOK FOR THESE FUN ITEMS:

☐ Ax
☐ Birch tree
☐ Chef
☐ Dynamite
☐ Elk
☐ Flowers (2)

☐ Geyser
☐ Legos
☐ Lynx
☐ Pig
☐ Puffin
☐ Scarecrow

☐ Sheep (2)
☐ Skiers (2)
☐ Tepee
☐ Viking
☐ Volcanoes (2)
☐ Wolf

NORTH
WEST
EAST
SOUTH

MOST OF NORTHERN EUROPE IS FLAT, EXCEPT FOR THE MOUNTAINOUS SCANDINAVIAN COUNTRIES.

GULF OF FINLAND

HELSINKI

ICE-BREAKER SHIP

STOCKHOLM

GOTLAND

OLAND

BALTIC SEA

THIS IS THE HOME OF SMORGASBORD... A MEAL CONSISTING OF MANY DIFFERENT HOT AND COLD DISHES.

WE EXPORT MACHINERY, AUTOS, WOOD AND PAPER PRODUCTS, AND PETROLEUM.

LAKE VATTERN

LAKE VANERN

VOLVO AUTOS

COPENHAGEN

THE LITTLE MERMAID STATUE IS HERE.

IN 1792, DENMARK BECAME THE FIRST EUROPEAN STATE TO ABOLISH SLAVE TRADING.

KATTEGAT

LEGOLAND

DENMARK

SKAGERRAK

OSLO

BAA!

OUR POPULATION IS 5,400,000 AND WE SPEAK DANISH.

NORTH SEA

OUR CHIEF AGRICULTURAL EXPORTS ARE DAIRY PRODUCTS AND HAMS.

THERE ARE NO MOUNTAINS IN DENMARK.

THE DANES PERFECTED THE FIRST DIESEL ENGINE AND, IN 1912, LAUNCHED THE FIRST OCEANGOING MOTOR SHIP IN THE WORLD.

WE PLANT OVER 100,000 SAPLINGS EACH YEAR TO MAINTAIN OUR FORESTS.

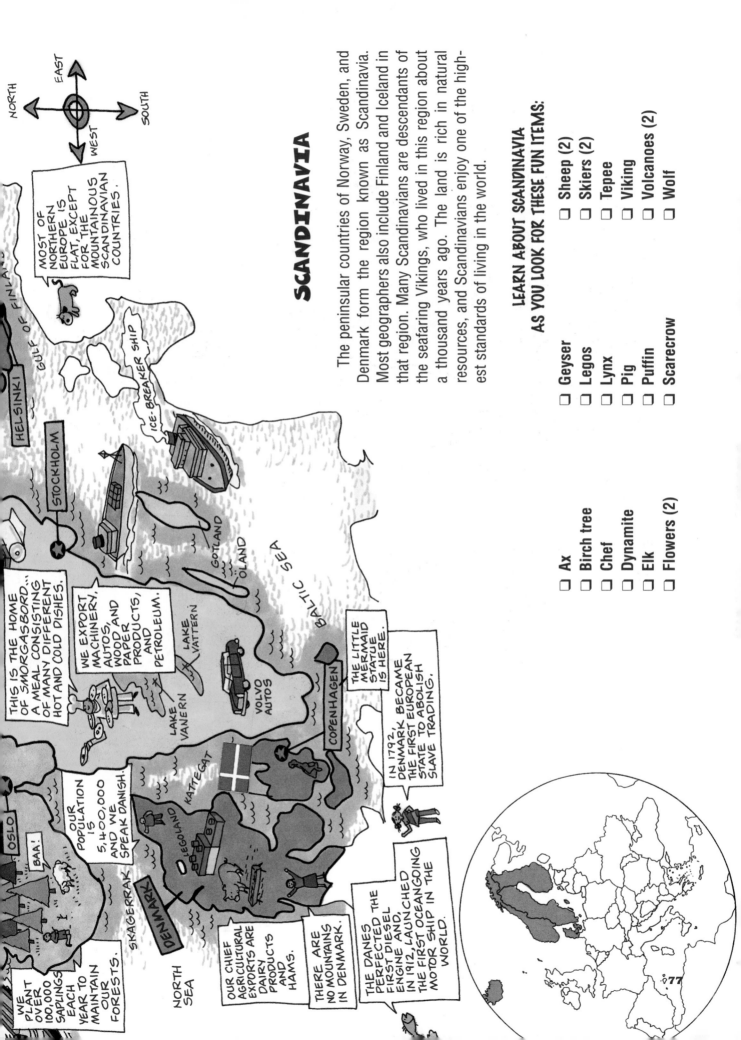

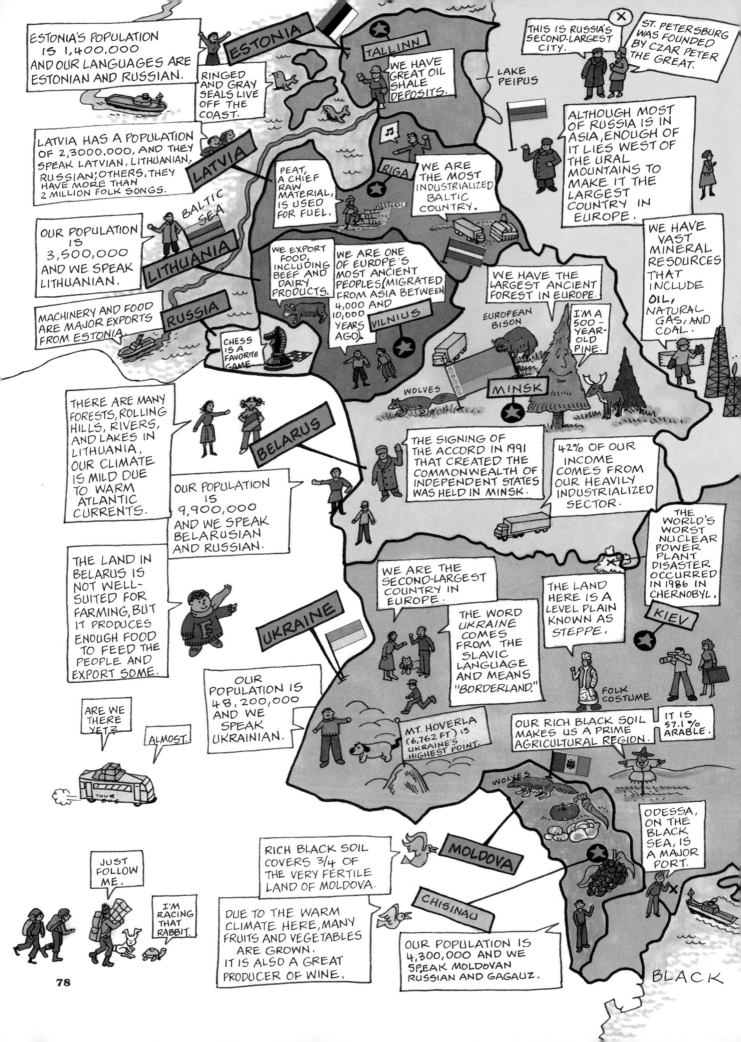

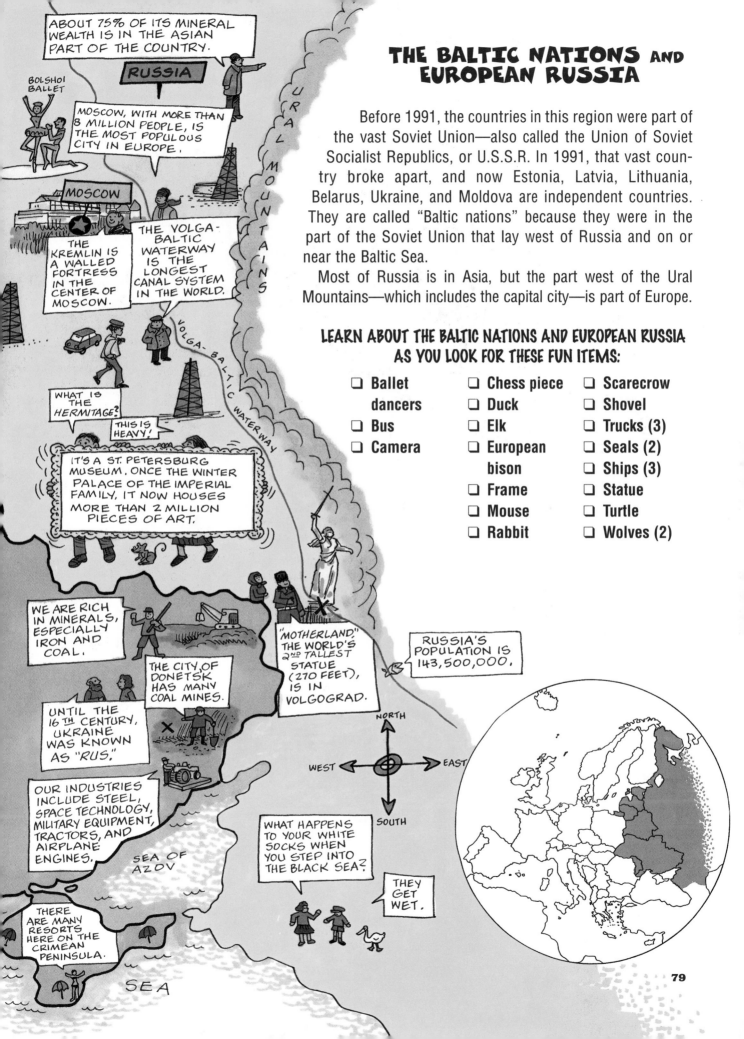

THE BALTIC NATIONS AND EUROPEAN RUSSIA

Before 1991, the countries in this region were part of the vast Soviet Union—also called the Union of Soviet Socialist Republics, or U.S.S.R. In 1991, that vast country broke apart, and now Estonia, Latvia, Lithuania, Belarus, Ukraine, and Moldova are independent countries. They are called "Baltic nations" because they were in the part of the Soviet Union that lay west of Russia and on or near the Baltic Sea.

Most of Russia is in Asia, but the part west of the Ural Mountains—which includes the capital city—is part of Europe.

LEARN ABOUT THE BALTIC NATIONS AND EUROPEAN RUSSIA AS YOU LOOK FOR THESE FUN ITEMS:

- ❏ Ballet dancers
- ❏ Bus
- ❏ Camera
- ❏ Chess piece
- ❏ Duck
- ❏ Elk
- ❏ European bison
- ❏ Frame
- ❏ Mouse
- ❏ Rabbit
- ❏ Scarecrow
- ❏ Shovel
- ❏ Trucks (3)
- ❏ Seals (2)
- ❏ Ships (3)
- ❏ Statue
- ❏ Turtle
- ❏ Wolves (2)

ABOUT 75% OF ITS MINERAL WEALTH IS IN THE ASIAN PART OF THE COUNTRY.

RUSSIA

BOLSHOI BALLET

MOSCOW, WITH MORE THAN 8 MILLION PEOPLE, IS THE MOST POPULOUS CITY IN EUROPE.

MOSCOW

URAL MOUNTAINS

THE KREMLIN IS A WALLED FORTRESS IN THE CENTER OF MOSCOW.

THE VOLGA-BALTIC WATERWAY IS THE LONGEST CANAL SYSTEM IN THE WORLD.

VOLGA-BALTIC WATERWAY

WHAT IS THE HERMITAGE?

THIS IS HEAVY!

IT'S A ST. PETERSBURG MUSEUM. ONCE THE WINTER PALACE OF THE IMPERIAL FAMILY, IT NOW HOUSES MORE THAN 2 MILLION PIECES OF ART.

WE ARE RICH IN MINERALS, ESPECIALLY IRON AND COAL.

THE CITY OF DONETSK HAS MANY COAL MINES.

"MOTHERLAND," THE WORLD'S 2ND TALLEST STATUE (270 FEET), IS IN VOLGOGRAD.

RUSSIA'S POPULATION IS 143,500,000.

UNTIL THE 16TH CENTURY, UKRAINE WAS KNOWN AS "RUS."

OUR INDUSTRIES INCLUDE STEEL, SPACE TECHNOLOGY, MILITARY EQUIPMENT, TRACTORS, AND AIRPLANE ENGINES.

SEA OF AZOV

NORTH

WEST   EAST

SOUTH

WHAT HAPPENS TO YOUR WHITE SOCKS WHEN YOU STEP INTO THE BLACK SEA?

THEY GET WET.

THERE ARE MANY RESORTS HERE ON THE CRIMEAN PENINSULA.

SEA

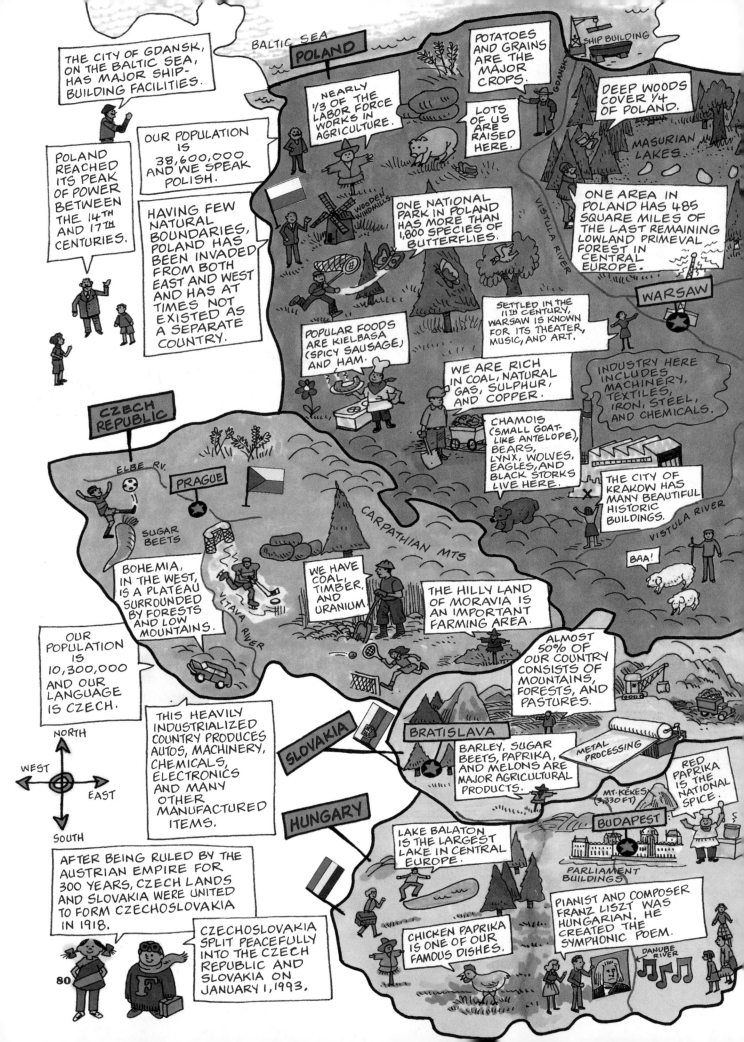

THE CITY OF GDANSK, ON THE BALTIC SEA, HAS MAJOR SHIP-BUILDING FACILITIES.

BALTIC SEA

POLAND

SHIP BUILDING

NEARLY 1/3 OF THE LABOR FORCE WORKS IN AGRICULTURE.

POTATOES AND GRAINS ARE THE MAJOR CROPS.

LOTS OF US ARE RAISED HERE.

DEEP WOODS COVER 1/4 OF POLAND.

GDANSK

MASURIAN LAKES

OUR POPULATION IS 38,600,000 AND WE SPEAK POLISH.

POLAND REACHED ITS PEAK OF POWER BETWEEN THE 14TH AND 17TH CENTURIES.

HAVING FEW NATURAL BOUNDARIES, POLAND HAS BEEN INVADED FROM BOTH EAST AND WEST AND HAS AT TIMES NOT EXISTED AS A SEPARATE COUNTRY.

WOODEN WINDMILLS

ONE NATIONAL PARK IN POLAND HAS MORE THAN 1,800 SPECIES OF BUTTERFLIES.

VISTULA RIVER

ONE AREA IN POLAND HAS 485 SQUARE MILES OF THE LAST REMAINING LOWLAND PRIMEVAL FOREST IN CENTRAL EUROPE.

WARSAW

POPULAR FOODS ARE KIELBASA (SPICY SAUSAGE) AND HAM.

SETTLED IN THE 11TH CENTURY, WARSAW IS KNOWN FOR ITS THEATER, MUSIC, AND ART.

WE ARE RICH IN COAL, NATURAL GAS, SULPHUR, AND COPPER.

INDUSTRY HERE INCLUDES MACHINERY, TEXTILES, IRON, STEEL, AND CHEMICALS.

CZECH REPUBLIC

ELBE RV.

PRAGUE

CHAMOIS (SMALL GOAT-LIKE ANTELOPE), BEARS, LYNX, WOLVES, EAGLES, AND BLACK STORKS LIVE HERE.

THE CITY OF KRAKOW HAS MANY BEAUTIFUL HISTORIC BUILDINGS.

VISTULA RIVER

SUGAR BEETS

CARPATHIAN MTS

BAA!

BOHEMIA, IN THE WEST, IS A PLATEAU SURROUNDED BY FORESTS AND LOW MOUNTAINS.

VLTAVA RIVER

WE HAVE COAL, TIMBER, AND URANIUM.

THE HILLY LAND OF MORAVIA IS AN IMPORTANT FARMING AREA.

OUR POPULATION IS 10,300,000 AND OUR LANGUAGE IS CZECH.

ALMOST 50% OF OUR COUNTRY CONSISTS OF MOUNTAINS, FORESTS, AND PASTURES.

NORTH

WEST

EAST

SOUTH

THIS HEAVILY INDUSTRIALIZED COUNTRY PRODUCES AUTOS, MACHINERY, CHEMICALS, ELECTRONICS AND MANY OTHER MANUFACTURED ITEMS.

SLOVAKIA

BRATISLAVA

BARLEY, SUGAR BEETS, PAPRIKA, AND MELONS ARE MAJOR AGRICULTURAL PRODUCTS.

METAL PROCESSING

RED PAPRIKA IS THE NATIONAL SPICE.

MT. KÉKES (3,330 FT)

HUNGARY

BUDAPEST

AFTER BEING RULED BY THE AUSTRIAN EMPIRE FOR 300 YEARS, CZECH LANDS AND SLOVAKIA WERE UNITED TO FORM CZECHOSLOVAKIA IN 1918.

LAKE BALATON IS THE LARGEST LAKE IN CENTRAL EUROPE.

PARLIAMENT BUILDINGS

80

CZECHOSLOVAKIA SPLIT PEACEFULLY INTO THE CZECH REPUBLIC AND SLOVAKIA ON JANUARY 1, 1993.

CHICKEN PAPRIKA IS ONE OF OUR FAMOUS DISHES.

PIANIST AND COMPOSER FRANZ LISZT WAS HUNGARIAN. HE CREATED THE SYMPHONIC POEM.

DANUBE RIVER

POLAND, CZECH REPUBLIC, SLOVAKIA, AND HUNGARY

When World War II ended in 1945, many countries in Eastern Europe came under the control of the Soviet Union. When the Soviet Union broke apart in 1991, the people in Poland, Czechoslovakia, and Hungary once again took charge of their own governments. In 1993, Czechoslovakia split into two independent countries, the Czech Republic and Slovakia.

LEARN ABOUT POLAND, CZECH REPUBLC, SLOVAKIA, AND HUNGARY AS YOU LOOK FOR THESE FUN ITEMS:

- ❑ Barn
- ❑ Bear
- ❑ Bird
- ❑ Bison
- ❑ Butterflies (4)
- ❑ Carrot
- ❑ Cooks (3)
- ❑ Flower
- ❑ Hockey player
- ❑ Music notes

- ❑ Pigs (2)
- ❑ Radio tower
- ❑ Sausage
- ❑ Scarecrows (5)
- ❑ Sheep
- ❑ Tennis ball
- ❑ Tourists
- ❑ Truck
- ❑ Windmill
- ❑ Woolly mammoth

THE NORTHEASTERN REGION IS DENSE WITH TALL TREES AND LAKES.

BUG RIVER

EUROPEAN BISON

PALACE OF CULTURE

OJCOW NATIONAL PARK IN THE SOUTH HAS 50 CAVES WHERE PREHISTORIC PEOPLE LIVED.

REMAINS OF PREHISTORIC MAMMOTHS HAVE ALSO BEEN FOUND THERE.

OUR POPULATION IS 5,400,000 AND OUR LANGUAGES ARE SLOVAK AND HUNGARIAN.

GOULASH, A TRADITIONAL HUNGARIAN DISH, IS A STEW OF MEAT, POTATOES, ONIONS, AND PAPRIKA (A SPICE MADE FROM SWEET RED PEPPERS), AND IS MY FAVORITE DISH TO MAKE.

WE'RE NOT LOST!

BECAUSE MOST OF OUR LAND IS FERTILE, HUNGARIANS PRODUCE ENOUGH FOOD TO FEED THE COUNTRY AND SELL ABROAD.

OUR POPULATION IS 10,100,000.

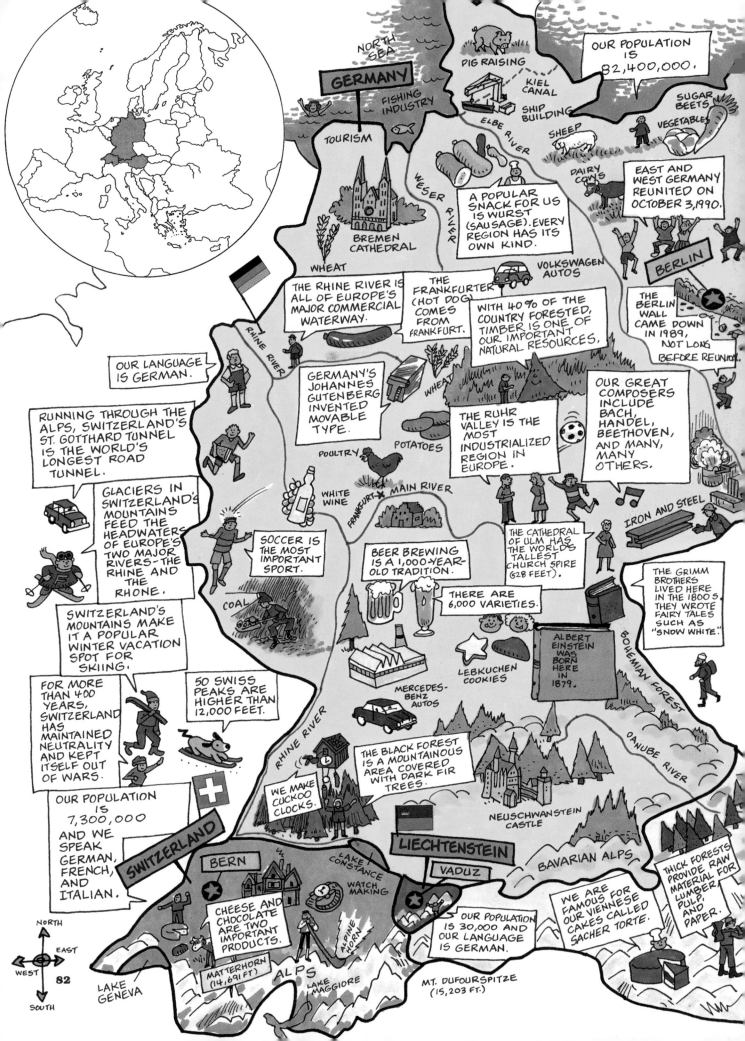

GERMANY

NORTH SEA

FISHING INDUSTRY

TOURISM

OUR POPULATION IS 82,400,000.

PIG RAISING

KIEL CANAL

SHIP BUILDING

ELBE RIVER

SHEEP

DAIRY COWS

SUGAR BEETS

VEGETABLES

EAST AND WEST GERMANY REUNITED ON OCTOBER 3, 1990.

BREMEN CATHEDRAL

WHEAT

WESER RIVER

A POPULAR SNACK FOR US IS WURST (SAUSAGE). EVERY REGION HAS ITS OWN KIND.

VOLKSWAGEN AUTOS

BERLIN

THE RHINE RIVER IS ALL OF EUROPE'S MAJOR COMMERCIAL WATERWAY.

THE FRANKFURTER (HOT DOG) COMES FROM FRANKFURT.

WITH 40% OF THE COUNTRY FORESTED, TIMBER IS ONE OF OUR IMPORTANT NATURAL RESOURCES.

THE BERLIN WALL CAME DOWN IN 1989, NOT LONG BEFORE REUNION.

RHINE RIVER

OUR LANGUAGE IS GERMAN.

GERMANY'S JOHANNES GUTENBERG INVENTED MOVABLE TYPE.

WHEAT

THE RUHR VALLEY IS THE MOST INDUSTRIALIZED REGION IN EUROPE.

OUR GREAT COMPOSERS INCLUDE BACH, HANDEL, BEETHOVEN, AND MANY, MANY OTHERS.

RUNNING THROUGH THE ALPS, SWITZERLAND'S ST. GOTTHARD TUNNEL IS THE WORLD'S LONGEST ROAD TUNNEL.

POULTRY

POTATOES

WHITE WINE

FRANKFURT MAIN RIVER

IRON AND STEEL

GLACIERS IN SWITZERLAND'S MOUNTAINS FEED THE HEADWATERS OF EUROPE'S TWO MAJOR RIVERS—THE RHINE AND THE RHONE.

SOCCER IS THE MOST IMPORTANT SPORT.

BEER BREWING IS A 1,000-YEAR-OLD TRADITION.

THE CATHEDRAL OF ULM HAS THE WORLD'S TALLEST CHURCH SPIRE (528 FEET).

THE GRIMM BROTHERS LIVED HERE IN THE 1800S. THEY WROTE FAIRY TALES SUCH AS "SNOW WHITE."

COAL

THERE ARE 6,000 VARIETIES.

SWITZERLAND'S MOUNTAINS MAKE IT A POPULAR WINTER VACATION SPOT FOR SKIING.

LEBKUCHEN COOKIES

ALBERT EINSTEIN WAS BORN HERE IN 1879.

BOHEMIAN FOREST

FOR MORE THAN 400 YEARS, SWITZERLAND HAS MAINTAINED NEUTRALITY AND KEPT ITSELF OUT OF WARS.

50 SWISS PEAKS ARE HIGHER THAN 12,000 FEET.

MERCEDES-BENZ AUTOS

RHINE RIVER

DANUBE RIVER

OUR POPULATION IS 7,300,000 AND WE SPEAK GERMAN, FRENCH, AND ITALIAN.

WE MAKE CUCKOO CLOCKS.

THE BLACK FOREST IS A MOUNTAINOUS AREA COVERED WITH DARK FIR TREES.

NEUSCHWANSTEIN CASTLE

THICK FORESTS PROVIDE RAW MATERIAL FOR LUMBER, PULP, AND PAPER.

SWITZERLAND

BERN

LAKE CONSTANCE

WATCH MAKING

LIECHTENSTEIN

VADUZ

BAVARIAN ALPS

CHEESE AND CHOCOLATE ARE TWO IMPORTANT PRODUCTS.

ALPINE HORN

OUR POPULATION IS 30,000 AND OUR LANGUAGE IS GERMAN.

WE ARE FAMOUS FOR OUR VIENNESE CAKES CALLED SACHER TORTE.

MATTERHORN (14,691 FT.)

ALPS

LAKE GENEVA

LAKE MAGGIORE

MT. DUFOURSPITZE (15,203 FT.)

GERMANY, SWITZERLAND, LIECHTENSTEIN, AND AUSTRIA

BALTIC SEA

TEXTILES

The countries of Germany, Switzerland, Liechtenstein, and Austria lie in an area sometimes known as central Europe. From north to south, this region's landscape changes from marshy plains to snowcapped moutains. It is crossed by two of Europe's longest rivers—the Rhine and the Danube—and by the Alps, the famous mountain range that is the longest and highest mountain range in western Europe.

LEARN ABOUT GERMANY, SWITZERLAND, LIECHTENSTEIN, AND AUSTRIA AS YOU LOOK FOR THESE FUN ITEMS:

- ❏ Alpine horn blower
- ❏ Automobiles (3)
- ❏ Ax
- ❏ Berlin Wall
- ❏ Books (3)
- ❏ Cake
- ❏ Carrot
- ❏ Chicken
- ❏ Coal miner
- ❏ Cookies
- ❏ Cows (2)
- ❏ Cuckoo clock
- ❏ Dogs (2)
- ❏ Great white heron
- ❏ Horse
- ❏ Hot dogs
- ❏ Pigs (2)
- ❏ Soccer ball
- ❏ Telescope
- ❏ Tuba
- ❏ Watch

HISTORICALLY, THE LAND OF GERMANY HAS BEEN MORE DIVIDED THAN UNITED, CONSISTING OF SMALL INDEPENDENT STATES.

AFTER GERMANY WAS DEFEATED IN WORLD WAR II, THE COUNTRY WAS DIVIDED INTO EAST AND WEST GERMANY. BERLIN WAS DIVIDED BY A CONCRETE WALL IN 1961. TODAY, GERMANY IS UNITED.

GERMANY IS ONE OF THE WORLD'S MOST INDUSTRIALIZED COUNTRIES. WE EXPORT AUTOS, MACHINES, CHEMICALS, ELECTRONICS, AND IRON AND STEEL PRODUCTS.

AUSTRIA

VIENNA OPERA HOUSE

WE ARE FAMOUS FOR OUR TRADITIONAL MUSIC.

VIENNA

OUR POPULATION IS 8,100,000 AND WE SPEAK GERMAN.

THE WORLD FAMOUS LIPIZZANER HORSES COME FROM AUSTRIA.

I'M A GREAT WHITE HERON FROM AUSTRIA.

WOLFGANG AMADEUS MOZART WAS BORN IN SALZBURG, AUSTRIA, IN 1756.

ABOUT 3/4 OF THE COUNTRY IS COVERED BY THE ALPS.

LIECHTENSTEIN WAS FOUNDED IN 1719 AND IS ABOUT THE SIZE OF WASHINGTON, D.C.

THE RHINE VALLEY COVERS 1/3 OF THE COUNTRY AND THE ALPS COVER THE REST.

LIECHTENSTEIN IS IN AN ECONOMIC UNION WITH SWITZERLAND. FOR MORE THAN 100 YEARS, THE COUNTRY HAS HAD NO ARMY, ONLY LOCAL POLICE.

THE HIGHEST PEAK IN AUSTRIA IS THE GROSSGLOCKNER (GREAT BELL), AT 12,461 FEET.

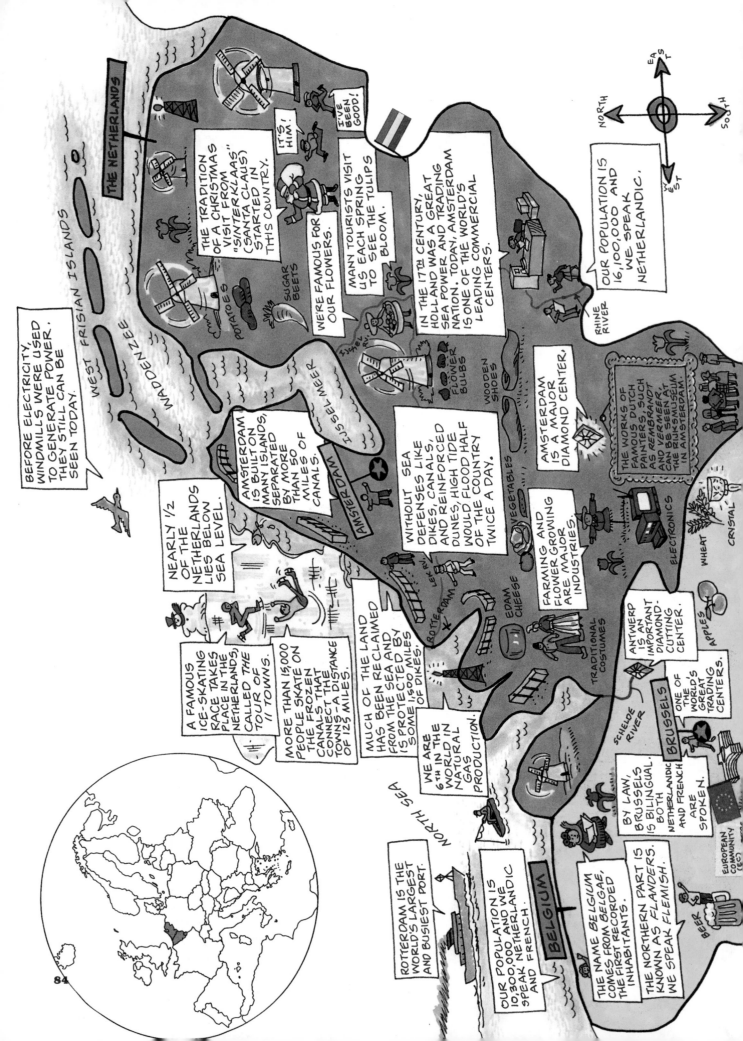

THE NETHERLANDS

WEST FRISIAN ISLANDS

BEFORE ELECTRICITY, WINDMILLS WERE USED TO GENERATE POWER. THEY STILL CAN BE SEEN TODAY.

WADDENZEE

THE TRADITION OF A CHRISTMAS VISIT FROM "SINTERKLAAS" (SANTA CLAUS) STARTED IN THIS COUNTRY.

IT'S HIM!

I'VE BEEN GOOD!

WE'RE FAMOUS FOR OUR FLOWERS.

POTATOES

SUGAR BEETS

MANY TOURISTS VISIT US EACH SPRING TO SEE THE TULIPS BLOOM.

IN THE 17TH CENTURY, HOLLAND WAS A GREAT SEA POWER AND TRADING NATION. TODAY, AMSTERDAM IS ONE OF THE WORLD'S LEADING COMMERCIAL CENTERS.

OUR POPULATION IS 16,100,000 AND WE SPEAK NETHERLANDIC.

IJSSEL MEER

ISSEL RV.

FLOWER BULBS

WOODEN SHOES

RHINE RIVER

NEARLY 1/2 OF THE NETHERLANDS LIES BELOW SEA LEVEL.

AMSTERDAM IS BUILT ON MANY ISLANDS, SEPARATED BY MORE THAN 50 MILES OF CANALS.

AMSTERDAM

WITHOUT SEA DEFENSES LIKE DIKES, CANALS, AND REINFORCED DUNES, HIGH TIDE WOULD FLOOD HALF OF THE COUNTRY TWICE A DAY.

AMSTERDAM IS A MAJOR DIAMOND CENTER.

THE WORKS OF FAMOUS DUTCH PAINTERS, SUCH AS REMBRANDT AND VERMEER, CAN BE SEEN AT THE RIJKSMUSEUM IN AMSTERDAM.

VEGETABLES

EDAM CHEESE

FARMING AND FLOWER GROWING ARE MAJOR INDUSTRIES.

ELECTRONICS

WHEAT

CRISTAL

A FAMOUS ICE-SKATING RACE TAKES PLACE IN THE NETHERLANDS, CALLED THE TOUR OF 11 TOWNS.

MORE THAN 15,000 PEOPLE SKATE ON THE FROZEN CANALS THAT CONNECT THE TOWNS—A DISTANCE OF 125 MILES.

LEK RV.

ROTTERDAM

MUCH OF THE LAND HAS BEEN RECLAIMED FROM THE SEA AND IS PROTECTED BY SOME 1,500 MILES OF DIKES.

WE ARE 6TH IN THE WORLD IN NATURAL GAS PRODUCTION.

TRADITIONAL COSTUMES

ANTWERP IS AN IMPORTANT DIAMOND-CUTTING CENTER.

APPLES

BRUSSELS

ONE OF THE WORLD'S GREAT TRADING CENTERS.

SCHELDE RIVER

NORTH SEA

BY LAW, BRUSSELS IS BILINGUAL. BOTH NETHERLANDIC AND FRENCH ARE SPOKEN.

EUROPEAN COMMUNITY (EC)

ROTTERDAM IS THE WORLD'S LARGEST AND BUSIEST PORT.

OUR POPULATION IS 10,300,000 AND WE SPEAK NETHERLANDIC AND FRENCH.

BELGIUM

THE NAME BELGIUM COMES FROM BELGAE, THE FIRST RECORDED INHABITANTS.

THE NORTHERN PART IS KNOWN AS FLANDERS. WE SPEAK FLEMISH.

BEER

NORTH
EAST
SOUTH
WEST

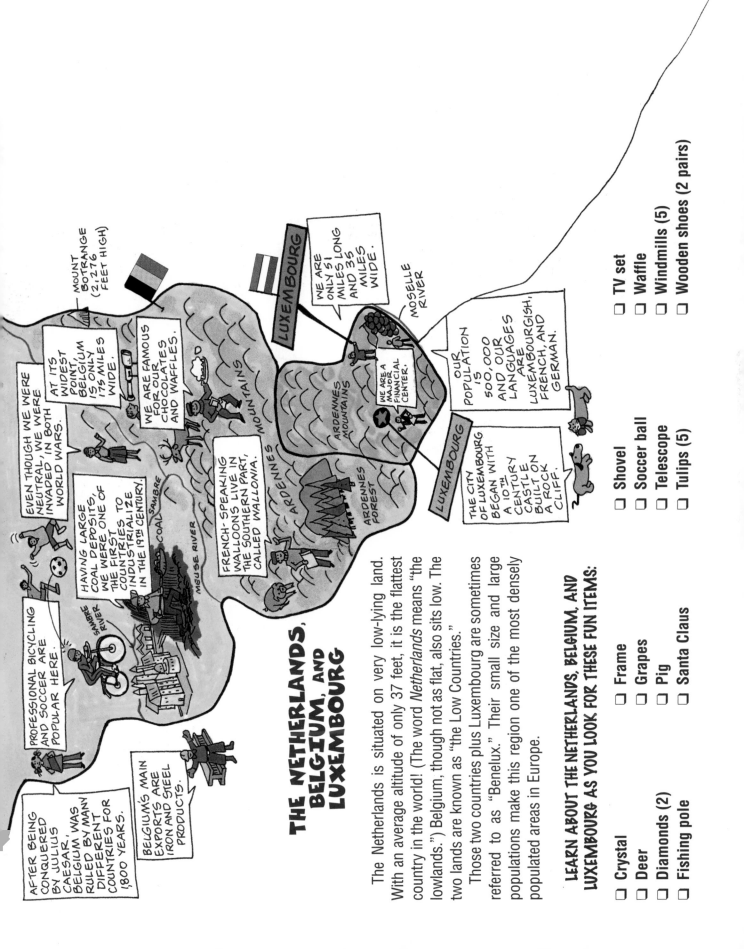

THE NETHERLANDS, BELGIUM, AND LUXEMBOURG

The Netherlands is situated on very low-lying land. With an average altitude of only 37 feet, it is the flattest country in the world! (The word *Netherlands* means "the lowlands.") Belgium, though not as flat, also sits low. The two lands are known as "the Low Countries."

Those two countries plus Luxembourg are sometimes referred to as "Benelux." Their small size and large populations make this region one of the most densely populated areas in Europe.

LEARN ABOUT THE NETHERLANDS, BELGIUM, AND LUXEMBOURG AS YOU LOOK FOR THESE FUN ITEMS:

- ☐ Crystal
- ☐ Deer
- ☐ Diamonds (2)
- ☐ Fishing pole
- ☐ Frame
- ☐ Grapes
- ☐ Pig
- ☐ Santa Claus
- ☐ Shovel
- ☐ Soccer ball
- ☐ Telescope
- ☐ Tulips (5)
- ☐ TV set
- ☐ Waffle
- ☐ Windmills (5)
- ☐ Wooden shoes (2 pairs)

FRANCE AND MONACO

France is one of the oldest countries in Europe. It also is one of the world's leading countries in terms of culture, historic and political influence, industry, and agriculture. The capital and cultural center is the city of Paris, nicknamed "the City of Light."

At France's southeastern corner lies Monaco, one of the world's smallest nations. (*Monaco* is also the name of its capital city.)

LEARN ABOUT FRANCE AND MONACO AS YOU LOOK FOR THESE FUN ITEMS:

- ❑ Apples (2)
- ❑ Artichoke
- ❑ Artist
- ❑ Automobile
- ❑ Chef
- ❑ Cyclist
- ❑ Dice
- ❑ Eels
- ❑ Eiffel Tower
- ❑ Geese (2)
- ❑ Mouse
- ❑ Musician
- ❑ Mustard
- ❑ Napoleon
- ❑ Paper airplane
- ❑ Perfume bottle
- ❑ Pig
- ❑ Red balloon
- ❑ Skier
- ❑ Snail
- ❑ Soccer ball
- ❑ Umbrellas (2)
- ❑ Walnuts

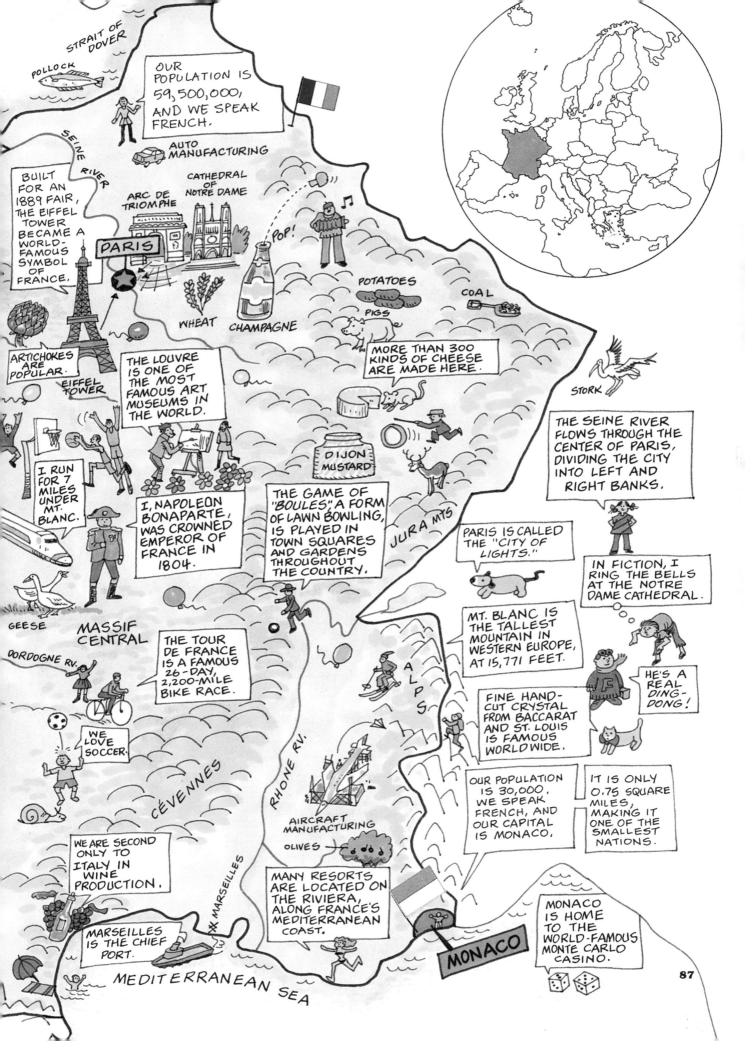

STRAIT OF DOVER

POLLOCK

OUR POPULATION IS 59,500,000, AND WE SPEAK FRENCH.

SEINE RIVER

AUTO MANUFACTURING

BUILT FOR AN 1889 FAIR, THE EIFFEL TOWER BECAME A WORLD-FAMOUS SYMBOL OF FRANCE.

ARC DE TRIOMPHE

CATHEDRAL OF NOTRE DAME

PARIS

POP!

POTATOES

PIGS

COAL

WHEAT

CHAMPAGNE

STORK

THE SEINE RIVER FLOWS THROUGH THE CENTER OF PARIS, DIVIDING THE CITY INTO LEFT AND RIGHT BANKS.

ARTICHOKES ARE POPULAR.

EIFFEL TOWER

THE LOUVRE IS ONE OF THE MOST FAMOUS ART MUSEUMS IN THE WORLD.

MORE THAN 300 KINDS OF CHEESE ARE MADE HERE.

DIJON MUSTARD

I RUN FOR 7 MILES UNDER MT. BLANC.

I, NAPOLEON BONAPARTE, WAS CROWNED EMPEROR OF FRANCE IN 1804.

THE GAME OF "BOULES," A FORM OF LAWN BOWLING, IS PLAYED IN TOWN SQUARES AND GARDENS THROUGHOUT THE COUNTRY.

JURA MTS

PARIS IS CALLED THE "CITY OF LIGHTS."

IN FICTION, I RING THE BELLS AT THE NOTRE DAME CATHEDRAL.

MT. BLANC IS THE TALLEST MOUNTAIN IN WESTERN EUROPE, AT 15,771 FEET.

HE'S A REAL DING-DONG!

GEESE

MASSIF CENTRAL

DORDOGNE RV.

THE TOUR DE FRANCE IS A FAMOUS 26-DAY, 2,200-MILE BIKE RACE.

A L P S

FINE HAND-CUT CRYSTAL FROM BACCARAT AND ST. LOUIS IS FAMOUS WORLDWIDE.

WE LOVE SOCCER.

RHONE RV.

OUR POPULATION IS 30,000, WE SPEAK FRENCH, AND OUR CAPITAL IS MONACO.

IT IS ONLY 0.75 SQUARE MILES, MAKING IT ONE OF THE SMALLEST NATIONS.

CÉVENNES

AIRCRAFT MANUFACTURING

OLIVES

WE ARE SECOND ONLY TO ITALY IN WINE PRODUCTION.

MARSEILLES

MANY RESORTS ARE LOCATED ON THE RIVIERA, ALONG FRANCE'S MEDITERRANEAN COAST.

MONACO

MONACO IS HOME TO THE WORLD-FAMOUS MONTE CARLO CASINO.

MARSEILLES IS THE CHIEF PORT.

MEDITERRANEAN SEA

87

THE IBERIAN PENINSULA

Spain, Portugal, and Andorra share a piece of land called the Iberian Peninsula. (A *peninsula* is a land area with water on all sides except for a neck of land connected to a larger landmass.) Spain and Portugal have long seafaring histories. Their explorers and settlers once ruled empires in Africa, Asia, North America, and South America. Tiny Andorra, tucked into an area of the Pyrenees Mountains, is landlocked.

Today, fishing, farming, and tourism are major industries in Spain and Portugal. More than 60 million tourists each year visit their historical cities and sun-drenched beaches.

LEARN ABOUT THE IBERIAN PENINSULA AS YOU LOOK FOR THESE FUN ITEMS:

- ❏ Anchovies
- ❏ Bottles (5)
- ❏ Brown bear
- ❏ Bulls (3)
- ❏ Cheese
- ❏ Cork
- ❏ Guitar
- ❏ Ibex
- ❏ Olive tree
- ❏ Skier
- ❏ Sunflowers (4)
- ❏ Umbrellas (3)
- ❏ Windmill
- ❏ Windsurfers (3)

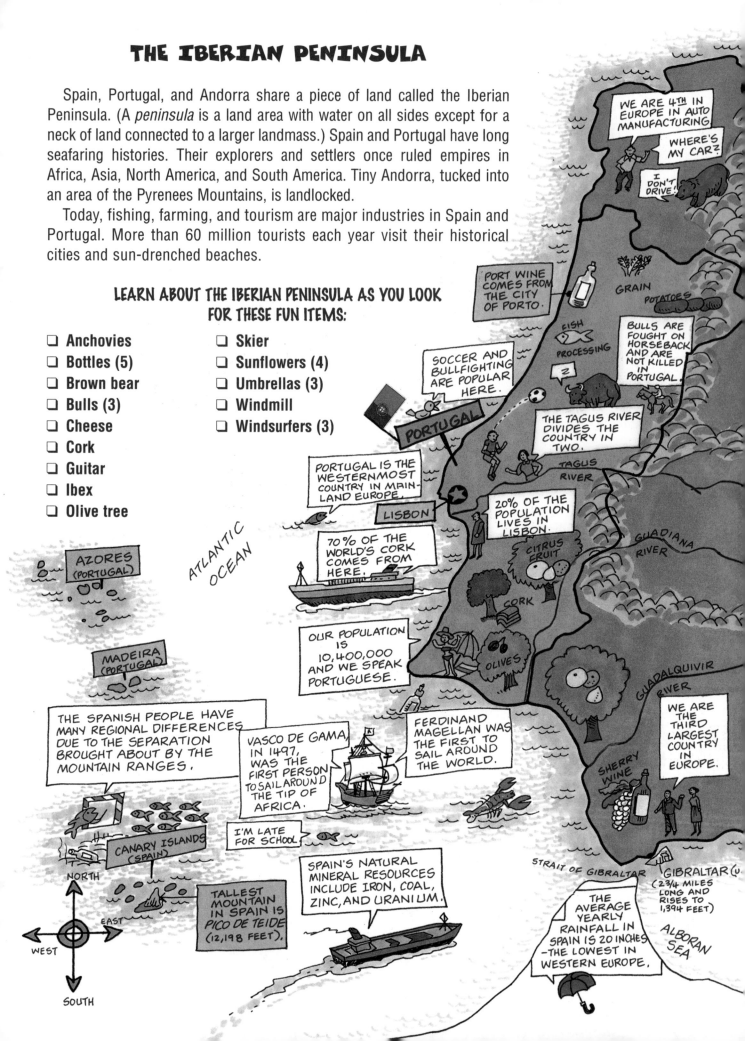

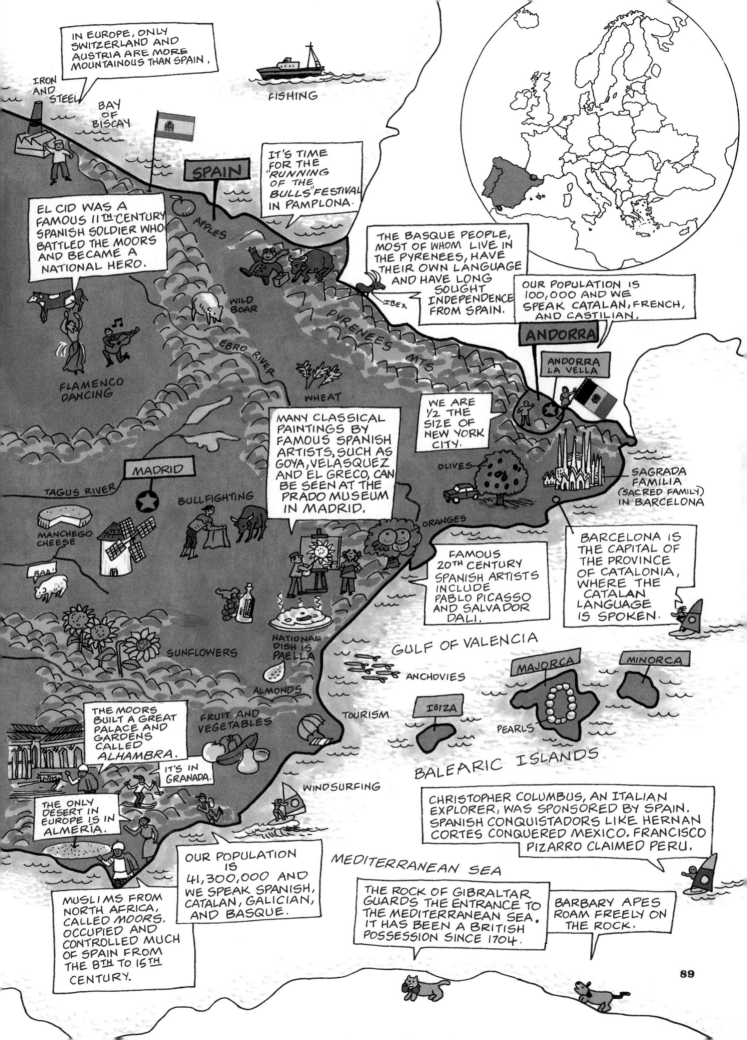

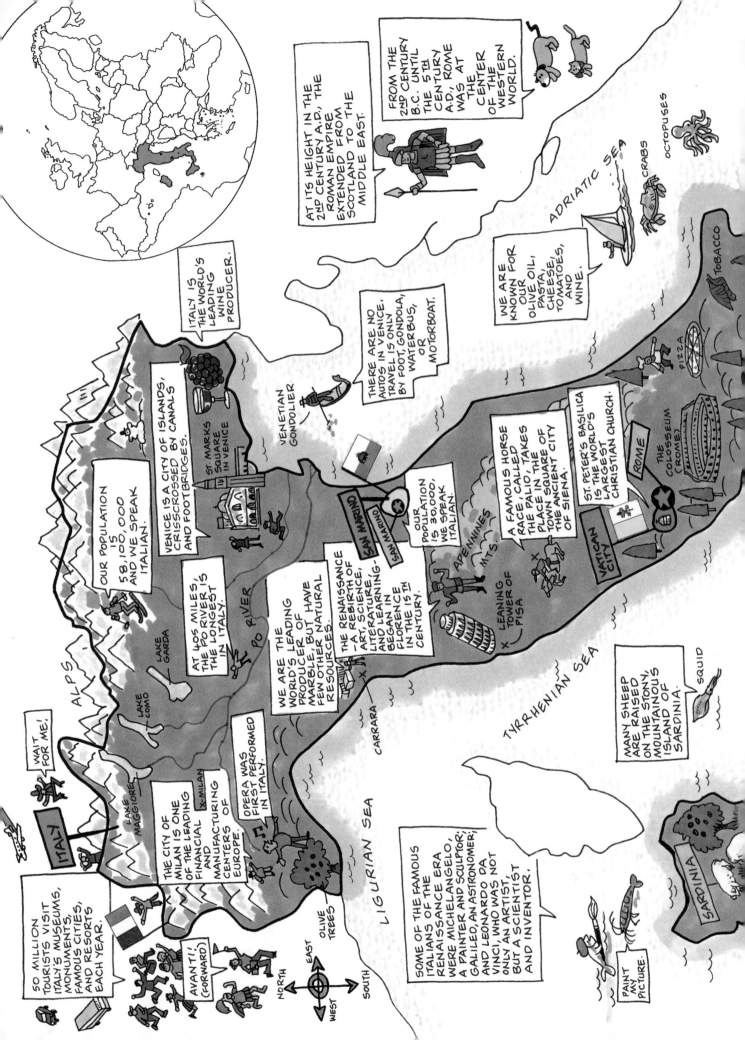

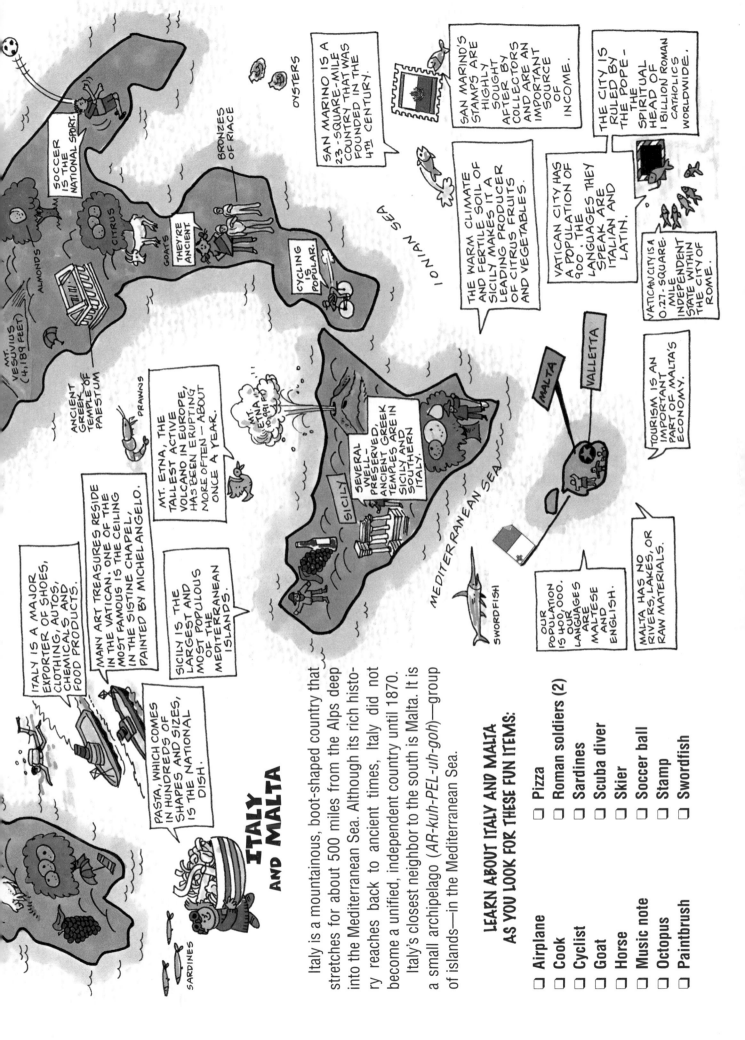

ITALY AND MALTA

Italy is a mountainous, boot-shaped country that stretches for about 500 miles from the Alps deep into the Mediterranean Sea. Although its rich history reaches back to ancient times, Italy did not become a unified, independent country until 1870. Italy's closest neighbor to the south is Malta. It is a small archipelago (AR-kuh-PEL-uh-goh)—group of islands—in the Mediterranean Sea.

LEARN ABOUT ITALY AND MALTA
AS YOU LOOK FOR THESE FUN ITEMS:

☐ Airplane
☐ Cook
☐ Cyclist
☐ Goat
☐ Horse
☐ Music note
☐ Octopus
☐ Paintbrush

☐ Pizza
☐ Roman soldiers (2)
☐ Sardines
☐ Scuba diver
☐ Skier
☐ Soccer ball
☐ Stamp
☐ Swordfish

SOCCER IS THE NATIONAL SPORT.

ALMONDS

MT. VESUVIUS (4,189 FEET)

CITRUS

GOATS

THEY'RE ANCIENT.

BRONZES OF RIACE

OYSTERS

SAN MARINO IS A 23-SQUARE-MILE COUNTRY THAT WAS FOUNDED IN THE 4TH CENTURY.

SAN MARINO'S STAMPS ARE HIGHLY SOUGHT AFTER BY COLLECTORS AND ARE AN IMPORTANT SOURCE OF INCOME.

THE CITY IS RULED BY THE POPE—THE SPIRITUAL HEAD OF 1 BILLION ROMAN CATHOLICS WORLDWIDE.

ANCIENT GREEK TEMPLE OF PAESTUM

PRAWNS

CYCLING IS POPULAR.

IONIAN SEA

THE WARM CLIMATE AND FERTILE SOIL OF SICILY MAKES IT A LEADING PRODUCER OF CITRUS FRUITS AND VEGETABLES.

VATICAN CITY HAS A POPULATION OF 900. THE LANGUAGES THEY SPEAK ARE ITALIAN AND LATIN.

VATICAN CITY IS A 0.27-SQUARE-MILE INDEPENDENT STATE WITHIN THE CITY OF ROME.

MT. ETNA, THE TALLEST ACTIVE VOLCANO IN EUROPE, HAS BEEN ERUPTING MORE OFTEN—ABOUT ONCE A YEAR.

MT. ETNA 10,991 FT.

SEVERAL WELL-PRESERVED, ANCIENT GREEK TEMPLES ARE IN SICILY AND SOUTHERN ITALY.

SICILY

MALTA

VALLETTA

TOURISM IS AN IMPORTANT PART OF MALTA'S ECONOMY.

MEDITERRANEAN SEA

OUR POPULATION IS 400,000. OUR LANGUAGES ARE MALTESE AND ENGLISH.

MALTA HAS NO RIVERS, LAKES, OR RAW MATERIALS.

SWORDFISH

ITALY IS A MAJOR EXPORTER OF SHOES, CLOTHING, AUTOS, CHEMICALS AND FOOD PRODUCTS.

MANY ART TREASURES RESIDE IN THE VATICAN. ONE OF THE MOST FAMOUS IS THE CEILING IN THE SISTINE CHAPEL, PAINTED BY MICHELANGELO.

SICILY IS THE LARGEST AND MOST POPULOUS OF THE MEDITERRANEAN ISLANDS.

PASTA, WHICH COMES IN HUNDREDS OF SHAPES AND SIZES, IS THE NATIONAL DISH.

SARDINES

THE BALKAN NATIONS

Much of this part of eastern Europe, known as the Balkans, was ruled by Turkey from the end of the 15th century until 1913. (The name *Balkan* comes from the Balkan Mountains of Bulgaria.) After World War I, several regions were combined to form Yugoslavia. It was heavily influenced by its huge neighbor, the Soviet Union. Soon after the Soviet Union broke apart in 1991, so did Yugoslavia. That land is now five independent countries: Serbia and Montegegro, Slovenia, Croatia, Bosnia and Herzegovina, and Macedonia.

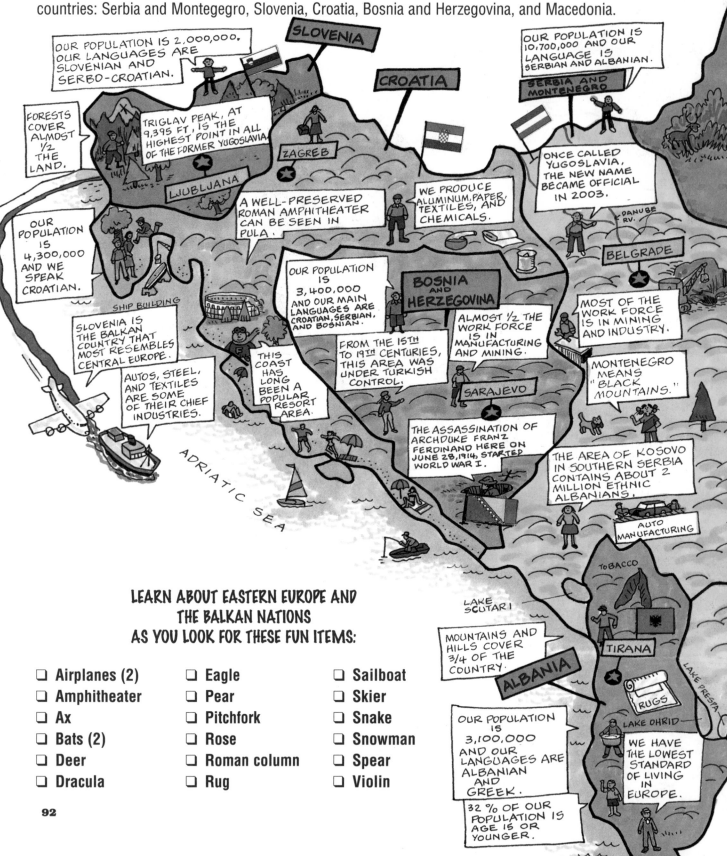

LEARN ABOUT EASTERN EUROPE AND THE BALKAN NATIONS AS YOU LOOK FOR THESE FUN ITEMS:

- ❑ Airplanes (2)
- ❑ Amphitheater
- ❑ Ax
- ❑ Bats (2)
- ❑ Deer
- ❑ Dracula
- ❑ Eagle
- ❑ Pear
- ❑ Pitchfork
- ❑ Rose
- ❑ Roman column
- ❑ Rug
- ❑ Sailboat
- ❑ Skier
- ❑ Snake
- ❑ Snowman
- ❑ Spear
- ❑ Violin

93

GREECE

The ideals of western democracy were born in Greece about 2,500 years ago. The art, philosophy, theater, mythology, science, and architecture that flourished there formed the basis of western civilization.

LEARN ABOUT GREECE AS YOU LOOK FOR THESE FUN ITEMS:
- ☐ Book
- ☐ Cotton
- ☐ Grapes
- ☐ Octopus
- ☐ Olympic torch bearer
- ☐ Sailboat
- ☐ Stone lion
- ☐ Telescope

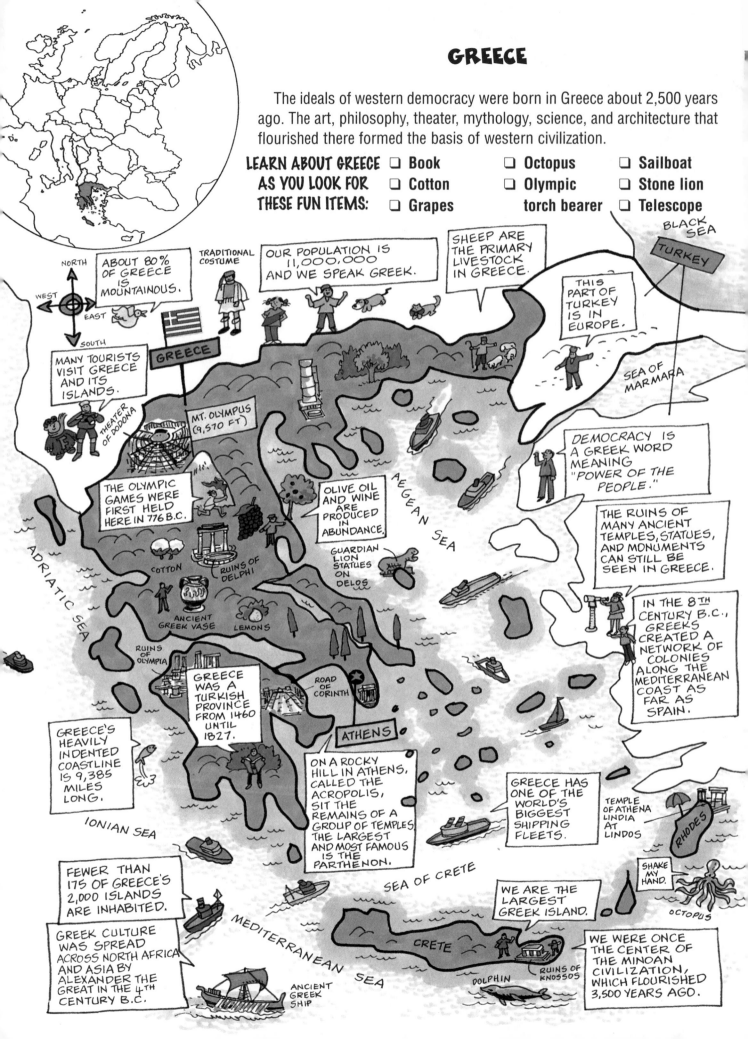

NORTH WEST EAST SOUTH

ABOUT 80% OF GREECE IS MOUNTAINOUS.

TRADITIONAL COSTUME

OUR POPULATION IS 11,000,000 AND WE SPEAK GREEK.

SHEEP ARE THE PRIMARY LIVESTOCK IN GREECE.

BLACK SEA

TURKEY

THIS PART OF TURKEY IS IN EUROPE.

GREECE

SEA OF MARMARA

MANY TOURISTS VISIT GREECE AND ITS ISLANDS.

THEATER OF DODONA

MT. OLYMPUS (9,570 FT)

DEMOCRACY IS A GREEK WORD MEANING "POWER OF THE PEOPLE."

THE OLYMPIC GAMES WERE FIRST HELD HERE IN 776 B.C.

OLIVE OIL AND WINE ARE PRODUCED IN ABUNDANCE.

AEGEAN SEA

THE RUINS OF MANY ANCIENT TEMPLES, STATUES, AND MONUMENTS CAN STILL BE SEEN IN GREECE.

COTTON

RUINS OF DELPHI

GUARDIAN LION STATUES ON DELOS

IN THE 8TH CENTURY B.C., GREEKS CREATED A NETWORK OF COLONIES ALONG THE MEDITERRANEAN COAST AS FAR AS SPAIN.

ADRIATIC SEA

ANCIENT GREEK VASE

LEMONS

RUINS OF OLYMPIA

GREECE WAS A TURKISH PROVINCE FROM 1460 UNTIL 1827.

ROAD OF CORINTH

GREECE'S HEAVILY INDENTED COASTLINE IS 9,385 MILES LONG.

ATHENS

ON A ROCKY HILL IN ATHENS, CALLED THE ACROPOLIS, SIT THE REMAINS OF A GROUP OF TEMPLES THE LARGEST AND MOST FAMOUS IS THE PARTHENON.

GREECE HAS ONE OF THE WORLD'S BIGGEST SHIPPING FLEETS.

TEMPLE OF ATHENA LINDIA AT LINDOS

RHODES

IONIAN SEA

FEWER THAN 175 OF GREECE'S 2,000 ISLANDS ARE INHABITED.

SEA OF CRETE

SHAKE MY HAND.

OCTOPUS

WE ARE THE LARGEST GREEK ISLAND.

GREEK CULTURE WAS SPREAD ACROSS NORTH AFRICA AND ASIA BY ALEXANDER THE GREAT IN THE 4TH CENTURY B.C.

MEDITERRANEAN SEA

CRETE

ANCIENT GREEK SHIP

DOLPHIN

RUINS OF KNOSSOS

WE WERE ONCE THE CENTER OF THE MINOAN CIVILIZATION, WHICH FLOURISHED 3,500 YEARS AGO.

INDEX OF COUNTRIES